TRANSATLANTIC PADDLE STEAMERS

BY THE SAME AUTHOR:

LIBRARIES FOR SCIENTIFIC RESEARCH IN EUROPE AND AMERICA. Grafton and Co., London, 1936.

ONE HUNDRED YEARS OF TRANSATLANTIC STEAM NAVIGATION. Science Museum: H.M. Stationery Office, London, 1938.

MARINE ENGINES. Science Museum: H.M. Stationery Office, London, 1938.

MERCHANT STEAMERS AND MOTOR-SHIPS. Science Museum: H.M. Stationery Office, London, 1949.

OUTLINE HISTORY OF TRANSATLANTIC STEAM NAVIGATION. Science Museum: H.M. Stationery Office, London, 1950.

TRANSATLANTIC PADDLE STEAMERS (Second Edition). Brown, Son and Ferguson, Ltd., Glasgow, 1967.

MARINE ENGINEERING. Science Museum: H.M. Stationery Office, London, 1953.

THE BIRTH OF THE STEAMBOAT. Charles Griffin and Co. Ltd., London, 1958.

SYNOPSIS OF HISTORICAL EVENTS: MECHANICAL AND ELECTRICAL ENGINEERING (Revision of Compilation by G. F. Westcott). Science Museum: H.M. Stationery Office, London, 1960.

STEAMSHIPS OF WAR. Science Museum: H.M. Stationery Office, London. In preparation.

PETIT GUIDE DU SCIENCE MUSEUM DE LONDRES. Science Museum: H.M. Stationery Office, London. In preparation.

PLATE I

P.S. "Savannah" (1818), the first auxiliary steamer
to cross the Atlantic; built at New York (see p. 15).

TRANSATLANTIC PADDLE STEAMERS

SECOND EDITION

BY

H. PHILIP SPRATT
B.Sc., A.S.M.E., I.S.O.

GLASGOW
BROWN, SON & FERGUSON, LIMITED
52 DARNLEY STREET

First Edition - 1951

Second Edition - 1967

Reprinted - 1980

ISBN 0 85174 158 4

© 1980 Brown, Son & Ferguson, Ltd., Glasgow G41 2SG
Made and Printed in Great Britain

PREFACE

Since this book first appeared, in 1951, the author has been able to complete another historical research, *The Birth of the Steamboat* (Griffin, 1958), which covers development from the first inventive aspirations and experiments in steam propulsion to the first steam vessel constructed of iron, and the first in all history to cross the Atlantic. This was, of course, the famous American auxiliary "Savannah" in 1819, and so our Second Edition of *Transatlantic Paddle Steamers* can now be read as a sequel to the earlier researches.

Fortunately the technical details of the "Savannah" were placed on record for all time in the contemporary illustrated *Mémoire sur les bateaux à vapeur des États-Unis d'Amérique*, compiled by Jean Baptiste Marestier, a French naval officer, and published at Paris in 1824. This work, available at the British Museum, London, has been consulted by the author, and from it have been taken the details of machinery shown in Plate II. A scale model of the vessel, exhibited at the Science Museum, in London, is illustrated in the Frontispiece.

The "Savannah" returned to America under sail alone, with her collapsible paddle-wheels stowed on deck; she did not function as a steamer on that occasion, and so it fell to a British vessel in 1821-22 to use steam on the Atlantic for the first time in a westerly direction. This was not the Liverpool-built "Conde de Palmella" mentioned in some of the history books, but the first British steam warship, built for the Earl of Dundonald at the time of the Chilean revolution. The pioneer steamers of the French, Dutch, and British navies followed soon after. The machinery for the last two was constructed by the famous London firm of Maudslay, Sons and Field, as was also that of the Dundonald paddle warship.

For the technical details of these early naval vessels, the author is indebted to contemporary documents preserved in the Archives Centrales de la Marine, and at the Bibliothèque Nationale, in Paris; for much other invaluable help, his thanks are also due to Contre-Amiral M. Adam, C.B.E., former French Naval Attaché in London;

to Monsieur le Capitaine J. Vichot, Directeur du Musée de la Marine, in Paris; to Miss J. B. van Overeem, Conservatrice at the "Prins Hendrik" Maritiem Museum in Rotterdam; and, of course, to the British Admiralty. The material of Chapter I was first presented by the author in October 1948, in the form of a Paper read before the Newcomen Society in London; it is reproduced here with their kind permission.

This pioneer or spasmodic phase ended with the transatlantic adventure of the Canadian "Royal William" in 1833, which the author has been able to reconstruct from contemporary and official documents placed at his disposal by Mr. E. C. Woodley, President of the Literary and Historical Society of Quebec; by Dr. Antoine Roy, Archivist at the Provincial Museum, Quebec; by Mr. G. R. Lomer, Librarian of McGill University in Montreal; and by Mr. William K. Lamb, Dominion Archivist, Ottawa. The "Royal William" could not have maintained continuous steam power across the Atlantic; her boilers were fed with sea water, prior to the invention of the marine surface condenser, and had to be cleared of salt every fourth day.

An achievement of the utmost importance in marine steam propulsion, was the invention of the surface condenser, by Samuel Hall in 1834. This enabled marine boilers to be fed with fresh water, and so kept in continuous operation. The first steamer on the Atlantic to be so fitted was the "Sirius" in 1838; and she, for the first time, maintained continuous steam power across the ocean. To mark this important centenary in April 1938, a Special Exhibition, prepared by the author, was held at the Science Museum in London; and scale models of the "Sirius" and the "Great Western" were constructed for the national collections.

This second phase, of sustained steam power across the Atlantic, was authoritatively chronicled at the time by Joshua Field, partner in the famous London firm of Maudslay, Sons and Field. His contemporary manuscript is still preserved in the Science Museum Library, and has been consulted for the technical data on most of the vessels described in Chapter II. It is noteworthy that Lieut. R. Roberts, R.N., who commanded the "Sirius" in 1838, went down with the "President" in 1841, the first steam liner to be lost on the Atlantic.

The third phase dates from the contract between Mr. Samuel Cunard and the British Post Office, for the transport of H.M. mails between this country and America. Of his first wooden steamer, the "Britannia," we have a non-technical but inimitable description from the pen of Charles Dickens, who crossed on her in 1842. Many first-class technical periodicals had been started about this time, and so we find these later paddle steamers of Chapter III to be much better documented than their predecessors. The sources of information, contemporary where possible, are indicated in the references. For particulars of the first Atlantic steamer named "United States," the author is indebted to Mr. John L. Lochhead, Librarian at the Mariners' Museum, Newport News; also to Mr. Forrest R. Holdcamper, of the United States National Archives.

The last chapter covers the transition from wood to iron, and from iron to steel, as the material for ship construction. Particulars of the famous "Great Eastern" have been taken from the description compiled by Mr. John Scott Russell himself, also from his monumental work on naval architecture. For details of the last paddle steamers built for the Atlantic service, the author has to thank Mr. G. C. Rhodes, Vice-Chairman of the French Line. In conclusion of Chapter IV, he is also much indebted to Mr. J. H. Iliffe, O.B.E., Director of Liverpool Public Museums, for particulars of the steel paddle steamers built at Liverpool and used on the Atlantic as blockade-runners in the American Civil War. The models illustrated in this book are those in the national collections at the Science Museum.

For quick reference and comparison, the technical data of the most important Atlantic paddle steamers are tabulated at the end of the volume. The author wishes to thank the Nautical Press most sincerely for their careful production of the book, also the friends who have helped to read the proofs and offer advice. Since the first edition appeared in 1951, substantial additions have been made, and some small errors corrected. However, in such a compilation of dates and technical detail, laboriously collected from scattered sources, the author dares never hope to have achieved complete freedom from error, despite all possible care. He would therefore welcome any further criticism, or authentic information, which would help to improve the accuracy or completeness of the book.

H. PHILIP SPRATT

Science Museum, London
April 1967

CONTENTS

LIST OF ILLUSTRATIONS

CHAPTER I

SPASMODIC PIONEERS

The nautical collections at the Science Museum, London, include a handsome scale model, presented by the Spanish Government, of the "Santa Maria" on which Christopher Columbus (1451-1506) sailed in 1492 for an unknown destination.[1] After the success of that immortal adventure, mariners knew for certain that a sail of two or three months westward across the Atlantic would take them to the New World.

As the years rolled by, what was once the saltiest adventure of the sea became more and more commonplace, until in 1710 the British Post Office mail packet service commenced operation. In 1816 the Black Ball Line, founded in New York, started their sail packet service to Liverpool; the crossing took 23 days eastward and 40 days westward. As the trade developed, so the vessels were improved, until the Atlantic service was maintained by a fleet of fast sail clippers[2] which was the pride of the mercantile marine about the middle of the nineteenth century.

In the meantime, however, the power of steam had been applied to paddle-wheel propulsion. The experimental period[3] extended from about 1775 to 1807, when Robert Fulton (1765-1815) achieved practical success with the P.S. "Clermont" on the river Hudson. In Europe the first steamer to run commercially was the P.S. "Comet," of about 28 tons burden, built in 1812 to the order of Henry Bell (1767-1830), which maintained a public service on the river Clyde. Her low-pressure steam engine, constructed by John Robertson (1782-1868), of Glasgow, is still preserved in the national collections at the Science Museum.

P.S. "SAVANNAH" (1818)

The first steam-propelled vessel to cross the Atlantic, or indeed any ocean, was the famous American auxiliary P.S. "Savannah" (see Plate I), built of wood at Corlears Hook, New York, by Samuel Fickett (1771-1840) and William Crockett, and launched on the

22nd August 1818. The vessel was at first intended for the sail-packet service to Havre, France; but before completion she was purchased by the newly-formed Savannah Steam Ship Co., and adapted for auxiliary steam propulsion with collapsible paddle-wheels.

The hull of the "Savannah" was carvel-built.[4] Her bow was convex and full above water, but finer below.[5] She carried a male bust head[6] above her cut-water, had a raked curved stem and a plain square transom stern, fitted with a narrow square-heeled rudder. The vessel carried three tall masts; her bowsprit was steeved well upward, as shown in a contemporary drawing,[7] to keep it out of the seas when the short hull pitched. The accommodation was divided into two main saloons, handsomely furnished. The state-rooms, with 32 berths, are said to have been commodious, and to have resembled those of a pleasure yacht rather than a steam packet.

To aid her considerable spread of sail, the "Savannah" was fitted with an auxiliary steam engine of 90 indicated h.p., constructed by Stephen Vail (1780-1864) at the Speedwell Iron Works, near Morristown, N.J. This had one cylinder 40 in. diam. by 5 ft. stroke, which was inclined at about 20 deg. so as to act directly onto the paddle shaft (see Plate II). The steam inlet and exhaust pipes were of equal bore, since there was no expansion in the cylinder, and the steam was discharged hot and at full pressure to the jet condenser. The air pump for this condenser worked on the same crosshead as the main piston rod.

Steam was supplied by low-pressure copper boilers with riveted flues, constructed by Daniel Dod (1778-1823), of Elizabeth, N.J. The pressure is said to have been less than 1 lb. per sq. in. above atmospheric. These boilers had to be blown out once a day, to avoid salt-water concentration. The engine and boiler spaces occupied most of the hold, from the main-mast to the fore-mast, so that little room was left for cargo.[8] The smoke pipe was fitted at the top with an elbow, which could be turned as necessary, to direct the smoke and sparks away from the sails.

The paddle-wheels were 15·25 ft. outer diam., and were made collapsible. Each had ten radial arms, held in position by a pair of chains near the outer ends, but which could be folded up like a fan and taken on deck when not in use. This operation could be performed in about 20 min. The paddle floats were 54 in. long and 32 in. wide, their outer corners chamfered. To prevent inboard

PLATE II

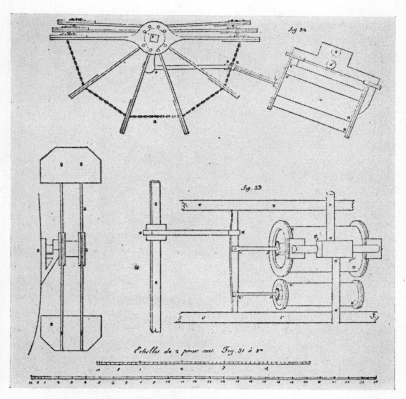

Machinery of the P.S. "Savannah" (1818), whose paddle-wheels could be folded up and taken on deck (see p. 16).

PLATE III

P.S. "Curaçao" (1825), built at Dover, the first steamer in the Netherlands Navy, and the first to cross the Atlantic under Dutch command (see p. 23).

splash, each paddle-wheel was provided with a removable canvas cover stretched over an iron frame (not shown in the illustrations). The wheels rotated at 16 revs. per min., and are said to have propelled the vessel, under steam power alone, at a speed of about 4 knots.

The "Savannah" ran her trials in March 1819 off Staten Island,[9] and was delivered soon after to her home port. The trade depression of that year, however, caused the Savannah Steam Ship Co. to abandon their proposal to use the vessel on coastwise service, and it was decided to send her to Europe for sale. She was advertised to sail for Liverpool, with an intermediate call at New York "should a sufficient number of passengers offer." None did in fact offer, and so the proposed call at New York was cancelled.

After numerous delays, the "Savannah" left her home port on the 24th May 1819, bound direct for Liverpool, under the command of her captain, Moses Rogers (1779-1821).[10] She carried no passengers,[11] but stowed 75 tons of coal and 25 cords of wood. The bulk of the fuel to be carried is said to have rendered the vessel unprofitable in service.[12] However, she persevered across the Atlantic, under sail with the occasional use of her paddles, at a mean speed of about 6 knots. On the 17th June she was seen off the coast of Ireland, and reported as a ship on fire. Her log-book[13] contains on the 18th June the admission: "No cole to git up steam."

However, she recoaled at Kinsale and steamed on to Liverpool, where she arrived on the 20th June. It was recorded[14] that: "The 'Savannah,' a steam vessel, recently arrived at Liverpool from America, the first vessel of the kind which ever crossed the Atlantic, was chased the whole day off the coast of Ireland by the 'Kite,' revenue cruiser on the Cork station, which mistook her for a ship on fire." The crossing from Savannah had taken 27 days 11 hrs., in which her paddle-wheels are said to have been used on seven occasions, for a total of about 85 hrs., and only when there was so little wind that her speed was reduced to 4 knots.

From Liverpool, the "Savannah" proceeded to Elsinore, Stockholm and St. Petersburg (now Leningrad) where it was hoped to sell her to Tsar Alexander I. It is said that the Tsar made a trip on board to Kronstadt; but he did not purchase her. The "Savannah" left Arendal, Norway, on the 22nd October,[15] and returned to her home port under sail, because of the high cost of coal abroad.[16] No attempt was made to use the engine, except as she entered the river Savannah on the 30th November 1819.

She left again on the 3rd December, and reached Washington in 12 days; but the U.S. Government did not purchase her. One newspaper[17] merely commented that her engine did not detract from her sailing qualities. In 1820 the vessel was sold at auction. Her engine was purchased by the Allaire Works, of New York, and she became a coastwise sail packet between Savannah and New York. She ran ashore on Long Island, in a gale of the 5th November 1821, and became a total wreck.[18] In 1944 the United States Post Office issued a commemorative "Savannah" stamp, of 3-cents face value.[19]

Principal dimensions of the P.S. "Savannah" were as follows:— Gross register, 320 tons; net, about 170 tons; length over all, about 110 ft.; length between perps., 98·5 ft.; breadth of hull, 25·8 ft.; breadth over paddle-wheels, when in use, about 36 ft.; depth of hold, 14·2 ft.; draught, about 13 ft.

P.S. "CONDE DE PALMELLA" (1820)

Now to be disposed of, once and for all, is that historical die-hard the P.S. "Conde de Palmella." This small paddle steamer of 70 tons burden, length 50 ft., and breadth 14 ft., was built by Messrs. Mottershead and Hayes, at Liverpool, and launched on the 26th September 1820, for Messrs. A. J. da Costa, of Lisbon. She was fitted with low-pressure condensing engines of 20 nominal h.p., constructed by Messrs. Fawcett (1772-1842) and Preston, of Liverpool, which are said to have propelled her at 3 knots in a calm. The vessel sailed from Liverpool in October 1820, under the command of Captain Silva, and arrived in Lisbon four days later. She is stated by several reputable steamship historians[20] to have proceeded thence to Brazil, but this cannot be substantiated.

Correspondence with the Director of the Biblioteca Nacional, at Lisbon, confirms that a local newspaper[21] contains an entry to the effect that a vessel named the "Conde de Palmella" arrived at Lisbon from Liverpool on Sunday, the 15th October 1820, with ballast. No evidence can be found in support of her reputed departure for Brazil; and further reference to the Biblioteca da Marinha, at Rio de Janeiro, has also failed to confirm her arrival in South America. In 1836, however, the British Consul at Lisbon reported the "Conde de Palmella" in use on the river Tagus;[22]

and therefore it seems evident that the transatlantic claims made on behalf of this British-built river steamboat must be dismissed.

P.S. "RISING STAR" (1821)

It would not be strictly accurate, and yet for practical purposes it would be sufficiently near the truth to say that it was a British steamer which first crossed the Atlantic westwards, from the Old World to the New. This apparent contradiction arises from the fact that when the famous American auxiliary P.S. "Savannah" (see p. 15) returned from Europe to her home port in 1819, she did so under sail alone. She did not function as a steamer on that occasion, but carried her collapsible paddle-wheels on deck.

The first authenticated steamship crossing of the Atlantic from east to west appears to have been that made in 1821-22 by the first British steam warship, the P.S. "Rising Star." This vessel had been ordered in 1818 by Thomas Cochrane (1775-1860), later the Tenth Earl of Dundonald, for use as a steam warship in the Chilean revolution; but not until 1820 was she laid down. The wooden hull was carvel-built by Daniel Brent, of Rotherhithe. The vessel had a rather bluff entrance, an extended parallel middle body with flat bottom and three keels, and a short run-in aft. She carried a figurehead above her curved raked stem, and had a plain square transom stern.

The vessel is stated first to have had one and a half, and later two, decks. An old print, published in 1821, represents her as a full-rigged ship with three masts, ten gun-ports on each side, and two funnels placed athwartships between the fore and main-mast. No side paddle-wheels or boxes are shown. The description attached to the picture states that the "Rising Star" was built "under the direction of Lord Cochrane upon the principle of navigating either by sails or by steam, the impelling apparatus being placed in the hold and caused to operate through apertures in the bottom of the vessel."

To aid her considerable spread of sail, the "Rising Star" was fitted with twin-cylinder engines of 70 nominal[23] and 120 indicated[24] h.p., constructed by Messrs. Maudslay, Sons and Field, of Lambeth.[25] Unfortunately, little is now known as to the precise nature of this machinery, but comparison can be made with a smaller but similar vessel, the P.S. "London Engineer," which was built in 1818 by

Daniel Brent and also fitted by Maudslay.[26] From this it would appear that the two vertical cylinders, about 42 in. diam. by 36 in. stroke, were placed athwartships, and each arranged to drive by means of bell-crank side-levers an overhung crank on either end of the paddle shaft. It is probable also that the bell-crank arms were equal, so that the inclined stroke of the connecting-rod was the same as the vertical stroke of the piston.

Steam at a pressure of about 2 to 3 lb. per sq. in. was supplied by marine flue boilers of the form in common use at that period; it is probable that four such boilers were used, two to each of the funnel uptakes placed athwartships. It is also possible that these boilers were made of copper, as were those of the "London Engineer," and the one fitted by Maudslay to the famous P.S. "Enterprise" in 1824. It was believed that copper boilers would stand up to continuous service better than iron, an important consideration where facilities for repair were not available. The boilers were, of course, fed with sea water, and had to be blown out occasionally to avoid salt concentration. At the low pressure used, no feed-pump was necessary; water could be run into the boilers from a raised tank. The funnels were tall and slender, about 2 ft. diam.

The two paddle-wheels, each about 13·5 ft. diam. and 7·5 ft. wide, were placed in the hold between the fore and main-mast, on either side of the centre keel. The wheels of the "London Engineer" had each eight radial floats, and were enclosed in an air-tight casing; this was open to the sea by apertures in the bottom of the vessel, between the centre keel and the two outer keels on either side. The paddle floats, about 39 in. wide, projected through these apertures, below the floor level to that of the three keels. As the paddle shaft was only about 15 in. above sea-level, two air pumps were used to force air into the casing and thus lower the water-level therein.

The "Rising Star" was floated out of dock on the 5th February 1821, and ran her trials in June, when a speed of 5 to 6 knots by steam power was attained on the Thames; the paddle-wheels would have made about 22 revs. per min. After many alterations and repairs had been made to her machinery, the vessel sailed from Gravesend on the 22nd October, bound for Valparaiso. She sprang a leak off the coast of Portugal, and put into Cork for repairs. She eventually arrived at Valparaiso in April 1822. The "Rising Star" is said to have proved herself "a very superior sea-boat" and often to have reached a speed of 12 knots. The extent to which she used steam power on the Atlantic, however, is not recorded.

By the time she arrived in Chile, the first steamer to enter the Pacific,[27] the revolution had succeeded, and the Spanish Navy had departed.[28] The "Rising Star" was therefore never used as a warship, for which she had been intended. In 1824 she was sold at Valparaiso to Messrs. Samuel Winter and J. Brittain, of Buenos Aires; and in 1827 she passed into the ownership of Mr. H. Stewart, of Liverpool. The vessel was wrecked in 1830.

Principal dimensions of the P.S. "Rising Star" were as follows:— Gross register, 428 tons; length between perps., 123·6 ft.; breadth, 27·8 ft.; depth of hold, 6·1 ft.; draught, about 5·5 ft.

P.S. "CAROLINE" (1823)

The paddle steamer "Caroline" of 1823 is not described, or even mentioned, in the standard works of our British historians such as Fincham, Lindsay, Kennedy, Holmes or Fletcher. She was however, notable as the first steamer in the French Navy,[29] and the second in all history to use steam on the Atlantic from east to west.[30] Her omission from British literature has doubtless been inadvertent, and due solely to the fact that the sources of information were not readily available to historians in this country.

Official records preserved in the Archives Centrales de la Marine, at Paris, establish it beyond doubt that this French steamer crossed the South Atlantic in 1824; but let us trace her history from the start. The vessel was built of wood by Messrs. Bataille et Malleux, at Rouen, to the plans of J. B. Marestier (1780-1832), and launched under the name of "Galibi" on the 23rd August 1823 for the merchant service. She was, however, renamed the "Caroline" in 1824, on her transfer to the French Navy, which she was the first steam-auxiliary vessel to enter.

The "Caroline" was a two-masted topsail schooner, and carried six guns. Her fore and main-mast, when first erected, were of 69 ft. and 72 ft. respectively; but both of them were shortened 6·5 ft. before she crossed the Atlantic. The hull is said to have had no keel;[31] but a false keel 10 in. deep was fitted later for ocean service.

To assist her spread of sail, and to enable the vessel to function as a tug-boat, the "Caroline" was fitted with low-pressure side-lever engines of 50 nominal h.p., ordered in December 1822 from Messrs. Manby, Wilson, Henry et Cie., of Charenton, near Paris,[32] and completed in 1824. The two cylinders were 29 in. diam. by 36 in. stroke, and could be disconnected from the paddle shaft at will. This enabled the paddle-wheels to turn freely, with the engines stopped, when the vessel was to proceed under sail alone, or when repairs to the machinery became necessary. The air pumps for the condenser were 19 in. diam.

Steam at a pressure of about 2 to 3 lb. per sq. in. was supplied by an iron flue boiler in three sections, each surmounted by a safety-valve. The three boiler sections were connected by two internal flues, fitted with muff-pieces to prevent the escape of smoke into the boiler-room. The paddle-wheels were 13·5 ft. diam.;[33] each had three sets of radial arms and carried six float boards 76 in. long and 23·5 in. wide.

The vessel, under the name of "Galibi," ran her trials in July 1824, with the Duchesse de Berry on board.[34] The paddle-wheels made 21 revs. per min., and a speed of 7 knots under steam power was attained. It is recorded that the engines ran smoothly and functioned perfectly; coal was consumed at the rate of 12·5 lb. per h.p. per hour.[35] After her transfer to the French Navy, the "Caroline" sailed from Brest on the 16th October 1824, under the command of Lieut. de Vaisseau M. Louvrier, bound for Cayenne. On the Atlantic she encountered head-winds which reduced her speed to 2 knots, and at times even to 1 knot. Off the coast of French Guiana, however, about 5 knots were maintained. The vessel arrived at Cayenne on the 21st November,[36] in 36 days, at a mean Atlantic speed of about 4·5 knots.

The "Caroline" arrived back in France on the 3rd August 1827. Her hull and machinery were inspected, and found to be in good condition, even though she had been under steam for more than 9000 hours. In 1828 the vessel was renamed the "Louise," and in 1829 she crossed to Cayenne for the second time. In November 1832 she was found to be in poor condition, and remained in French Guiana as a hulk until 1833, when she was condemned and broken up.[37]

Principal dimensions of the P.S. "Caroline" were as follows:— Gross register, about 350 tons; net, 200 tons; length between perps., 121·3 ft.; breadth of hull, 23 ft.; breadth over paddle boxes, about 39 ft.; depth in hold, about 6 ft.; draught, with false keel, 5·5 ft.

P.S. "CURAÇAO" (1825)

The wooden hull of this paddle steamer was built at Dover, by Messrs. J. H. and J. Duke, and launched in September 1825 under the name of "Calpe." The vessel was intended for trade between Great Britain, America and the West Indies, by the American and Colonial Steam Navigation Co., of London. She never sailed in their service, however, for in October 1826 she was sold to the Dutch, complete with all appurtenances. Renamed by them the "Curaçao," she became the first steamship in the Netherlands Navy.

The hull was carvel-built, to rather full underwater lines, with a bluff entrance, no parallel middle body, and a long run aft. The paddle-wheels were placed well forward, and the upper strakes of the hull were flared out, to increase the deck space and reduce the projection of the sponsons. The vessel carried a scroll head above her round cut-water bow, a feature found only in a few of the earlier steamships and abandoned by about 1850. She had one flush deck, raised about 10 in. at the square stern, which was decorated with mock quarters.

The "Curaçao" was schooner-rigged, with three masts and a standing bowsprit (see Plate III). She was at first armed with two iron 12-pr. carronades by the Netherlands Navy; but this armament was later increased to five 36-prs., one pivoted forward of the mizzen-mast, and two 6-prs. The crew consisted of 42 officers and men.

To assist her spread of sail, the "Curaçao" was propelled by side-lever engines of 100 nominal h.p., constructed by Messrs. Maudslay, Sons and Field, of London. These had two cylinders, 40 in. diam. by 48 in. stroke,[38] and could have developed about 150 indicated h.p. The condensers maintained a vacuum of 26 to 27 in. Steam at a pressure of 3 lb. per sq. in. was supplied by a rectangular iron boiler with four furnaces, which was tested to 6 lb. per sq. in. pressure. No feed-pump was necessary; water was run into the boiler from a raised tank. Coal was stowed in two iron bunkers on either side of the engine-room and in another bunker aft. The total coal reserve was later increased to about 95 tons by the addition of two timber bunkers built in above the sides of the boiler.

The paddle shafts were fitted with worm-operated disconnecting cranks of the form introduced by Henry Maudslay (1771-1831).

These enabled the paddle-wheels to turn freely, with the engines stopped, when the vessel was to proceed under sail alone, or when repairs to the machinery became necessary. The paddle-wheels were 15 ft. rim diam.; each was fitted with 14 fixed radial floats, about 7 ft. long and 2 ft. wide. The float width was later reduced to 18 in. The paddle-wheels rotated at 22 revs. per min., and the normal speed of the vessel was about 8 knots.

Under the command of First-Lieut. J. W. Moll, the "Curaçao" sailed from Hellevoetsluis, near Rotterdam, on the 26th April 1827, bound for Paramaribo with a total of 57 persons on board. The journal of her Atlantic crossing, preserved in the archives of the Dutch Departement der Marine, relates in detail the mechanical difficulties with which the commander had to contend.[39] Often the engines had to be stopped, to replace lost paddle floats; often the fires had to be put out, to clean and repair the leaking boiler, encrusted with salt. As the coal was consumed, at about 5 tons per day under full steam, and the vessel rose, her paddle-wheels were increased, first to 16 ft. diam. by additional floats 6 in. wide placed outside the rims, and then further to 17 ft. diam. by a redisposition of the main 18-in. floats. Before the eventual return to Hellevoetsluis, some 30 paddle floats had been lost and replaced.

Moll seems, however, to have been mainly concerned with the "lurching" of the vessel. Her best speed, with favourable winds, was 10 knots. On the 23rd May, the coast of Guiana was sighted; and next afternoon the "Curaçao" anchored in Paramaribo. The crossing, of about 4000 sea miles, had taken 28 days at a mean speed of 6 knots, with the intermittent help of her paddle-wheels.

After her return to Hellevoetsluis, the "Curaçao" was fitted with bilge keels, which helped to cure the lurching. For her second crossing, she left Holland on the 1st March 1828 with 68 on board, and reached Paramaribo in 25 days, for the first 13 of which she maintained continuous steam power. After her third double crossing, in 1829, the "Curaçao" was withdrawn from the West-Indies service, and remained from 1830 to 1834 stationed on the Schelde. In this period she made a trip to London, and once more in 1839. Then from 1840 she returned for a time on the West-Indies station, until decommissioned in 1846. She never sailed again, and in 1850 her hulk was sold to the shipbreakers.

Principal dimensions of the P.S. "Curaçao" were as follows:—
Gross register, 438 tons; net, 239 tons; length on deck, from stem

to sternpost, 130·5 ft.; length between perps., 127·3 ft.; length of keel, 114·7 ft.; breadth of hull, 26·9 ft.; breadth over paddle boxes, 44·9 ft.; depth of hold, 16·5 ft.; draught, about 13·5 ft.

P.S. "RHADAMANTHUS" (1832)

The first steam vessel of the British Navy to cross the Atlantic was the "Rhadamanthus," built of wood by the Admiralty at Devonport, to the plans of Mr. T. Roberts, and launched in April 1832. Four sister-ships were also built about the same time. The "Rhadamanthus" was the first steam vessel to be built at Devonport, and was commissioned in October 1832.

She was described at the time as "beautiful to look at, and as sharp in the bow as the bill of a snipe." She carried four guns, a complement of 60 officers and men, and was schooner-rigged with three masts and a standing bowsprit. Her paddle-wheels were placed well forward, and were driven by side-lever engines of 220 nominal h.p., constructed by Messrs. Maudslay, Sons and Field, of London.[40] These had two cylinders, 55·5 in. diam. by 5 ft. stroke, which developed 385 indicated h.p. on trial. Steam was supplied at a pressure of 3·5 lb. per sq. in. by iron tubular boilers. The paddle-wheels were 20 ft. diam., each with 12 fixed radial floats, and rotated at 18 revs. per min. The normal speed of the vessel was about 8 knots.

The "Rhadamanthus" was used for a time with her sister-ship, the P.S. "Dee" (1832), in a blockade of the Dutch coast, and was then sent to the West Indies. She left Plymouth on the 21st April 1833, and steamed across the Bay of Biscay. Her engines were then stopped, and with six floats removed from each paddle-wheel, she continued to Funchal under sail alone. Her coal bunkers were replenished to about 320 tons at Madeira, where she left on the 30th April for Barbados. Steam power was used intermittently; the floats of her paddle-wheels were removed and replaced as required. Barbados was reached on the 17th May; the distance of 2500 miles was covered at a mean speed of 6·1 knots.

The "Rhadamanthus" was later used at Port Royal, Jamaica, to make a survey and to place buoys. She left there on the 11th February 1834, and arrived back in Plymouth on the 3rd April.[41] In 1849 her captain, W. H. Henderson,[42] pronounced her "an excellent sea boat, and a very serviceable vessel." In 1860 her boilers were fitted with superheaters. The vessel was broken up at Sheerness in 1864.

Principal dimensions of the "Rhadamanthus" were as follows:— Old measurement, 813 tons; length over all, about 190 ft.; length between perps., 164·6 ft.; length of keel, 143·2 ft.; breadth of hull, 32·7 ft.; breadth over paddle boxes, about 51 ft.; depth of hold, 17·8 ft.; draught, 14·5 ft.

P.S. "ROYAL WILLIAM" (1831)

This famous Canadian paddle steamer was built of wood at Quebec[43] by Messrs. Black and Campbell, to the plans of their naval architect and foreman, Mr. James Goudie (1809-1892). The keel was laid in September 1830 at Cape Cove, a mile above the Citadel, near the spot where Wolfe breathed his last. The vessel was named after William IV, and launched on the 27th April 1831.[44] Two years later she made history as the first Canadian steamship to cross the Atlantic.

The wooden hull was carvel-built to the lines by Mr. James Goudie, who had learned his profession in Scotland. The vessel had a fine entrance, and a short parallel middle body between the paddle boxes. The upper strakes of the hull were flared out, fore and aft, to envelop and protect the paddle-wheels; there were no outboard sponsons. The vessel carried a scroll head above her cut-water bow. She had one flush deck, and her square stern was decorated with mock quarters.

The "Royal William" was schooner-rigged, with three tall masts and a standing bowsprit (see Plate IV). She carried three square sails on the fore-mast. The underdeck cabin is said to have been fitted out tastefully, and to have contained some 50 berths. The dining saloon occupied the round house on deck. Accommodation was also provided for about 80 steerage passengers. The crew consisted of 36 men.

After her launch, the "Royal William" was towed up the river St. Lawrence to Montreal, to be fitted with side-lever engines of 200 nominal h.p. by Messrs. Bennet and Henderson. The senior partner of this firm, John Bennet (1791-1849), was born in Scotland,[45] and had served his apprenticeship with Messrs. James Watt and Co. The engines of the "Royal William" comprised two cylinders, about 51 in. diam. by 60 in. stroke, which could have developed about

300 indicated h.p. The crankshafts were forged by Robert Napier (1791-1876), in his works at Glasgow.[46]

Steam at a pressure of about 4 lb. per sq. in. was supplied by flat-sided rectangular iron boilers of the form in common use at that period. The paddle-wheels were 18·5 ft. diam., and rotated at about 20 revs. per min. Each was fitted with 15 fixed radial floats 6·25 ft. long and 21 in. wide. The normal speed of the vessel would be about 8 knots.

The "Royal William" was intended to improve communication between the maritime provinces of Old Canada by the newly-formed Quebec and Halifax Steam Navigation Co., with which Samuel Cunard (1787-1865) and his brothers were associated. In 1831 she made three round trips from Quebec to Halifax and intermediate ports. In 1832, however, the vessel had to be quarantined on account of the cholera epidemic, and the Company suffered heavy financial loss. Early in 1833 the "Royal William" was sold, and later despatched by her new owners to Boston, where she was received enthusiastically on the 17th June as the first British steamer to enter a port of the United States. On her return to Quebec, it was decided to send the vessel to London for sale.

The "Royal William" left Pictou harbour, Nova Scotia, on the 18th August 1833, with seven passengers on board, and heavily laden with 324 tons of coal.[47] She encountered a gale off New-foundland, which disabled the starboard engine, and the vessel was reported to be sinking. However, the pumps were started, and she ran for ten days on the port engine alone. She persevered across the Atlantic, at a mean speed of about 6 knots, and on the 6th September put into Cowes for repairs. She then continued round to the Thames, and eventually reached her destination at Gravesend on the 12th September, after 25 days from Pictou. It has been said that most of her crossing was made under steam power, apart of course from the intervals necessary to clear the boilers of salt, which in the words[48] of her captain, John McDougall, occupied "from 24 to 26 hours every fourth day."

The "Royal William" was chartered to the Portuguese Government soon after her arrival in London; and in September 1834 she was sold to the Spanish, and converted into a warship under the name of "Isabella Segunda." She was the first steamer in the Spanish Navy.[49] In 1840 she was sent to Bordeaux for repairs, but her timbers had become rotten, and she was converted into a hulk.[50]   Another vessel of the same name was built at Bordeaux to receive her engines,[51] but this was wrecked in January 1860 off the coast of Algeria.

Philatelists will be interested to note that in August 1933 the Canadian Post Office issued a special "Royal William" stamp,[52] to mark the centenary of her historic Atlantic adventure. The stamp represents the vessel at sea, under full steam, and is of 5-cents face value.

Principal dimensions of the P.S. "Royal William" (1831) were as follows:—Gross measurement, 1370 tons;[53] net, 363 tons; length of deck, 176 ft.; length between perps., 160 ft.; length of keel, 146 ft.; breadth between paddle boxes, 28 ft.; breadth over all, 44 ft.; depth of hold, 17·75 ft.; draught, 14 ft. Her transatlantic adventure of 1833 concludes this first spasmodic phase. Not until five years later was the Atlantic crossed under continuous steam power, thanks to the surface condenser patented by Samuel Hall, which (as described in the next chapter) enabled marine boilers to be fed with fresh water and thus kept in constant operation.

CHAPTER II

SUSTAINED STEAM POWER

The vessels described in the previous chapter could not be termed "steamers" in the full sense. The "Savannah" availed herself of steam power, with removable paddle-wheels, only on those rare occasions when the Atlantic winds failed her. In 1820 it seemed improbable that steam could ever be found practicable as the motive power to propel ships across an ocean;[54] indeed the scholars of those times proceeded to demonstrate by scientific calculation that no vessel could carry sufficient coal to steam across the Atlantic.

In 1833, however, we find that the "Royal William" could easily have done so, had it not been necessary to blow out her boilers every fourth day to clear them of salt concentration. The boilers of all those "spasmodic pioneers" had to be fed with sea water, to the detriment of their iron plates, where copper was not used, and to their periodical encumbrance with salt. The first practical surface condensers, patented by Samuel Hall (1781-1863) in 1834,[55] however, enabled marine boilers to be fed with fresh distilled water, and thus kept in constant operation.

This second phase, that of the more determined use of sustained steam power from port to port, was heralded in by the P.S. "Sirius" and "Great Western" in April 1838, and was authoritatively chronicled at the time by Joshua Field (1787-1863), a partner in the famous London firm of Maudslay, Sons and Field. His contemporary manuscript document,[56] preserved in the Science Museum Library, has been consulted for much of the technical detail recorded in this chapter.

P.S. "SIRIUS" (1837)

The first vessel to cross the Atlantic under continuous steam power was the "Sirius." She was built of wood in 1837 by Messrs. Robert Menzies and Son, at Leith, for the service between London and Cork of the St. George Steam Packet Co., which eventually became the City of Cork Steam Packet Co. Although never intended for the Atlantic service, this little cross-channel steamer was chartered by the newly-formed British and American Steam Navigation Co., whose own vessel, the P.S. "British Queen" (see p. 34), was not completed in time, and despatched from Cork Harbour to New York in April 1838.

The "Sirius" was a two-masted vessel (see Plate V). Three square sails were carried on the fore-mast, while the main-mast was rigged fore-and-aft. The figurehead consisted of a dog, holding between its front paws the Dog Star, Sirius, after which the vessel was named.[57] The crew consisted of 35 officers and men.

The vessel was propelled by side-lever engines of 320 nominal h.p., constructed by Messrs. Thomas Wingate and Co., of Whiteinch near Glasgow, with two cylinders 60 in. diam. by 6 ft. stroke.[58] She was the first steamer on the Atlantic to be fitted with surface condensers, patented by Samuel Hall in 1834, which enabled her boilers to be fed with fresh water. Steam at a pressure of 5 lb. per sq. in. was supplied by rectangular flue boilers, which consumed about 24 tons of coal per day. The paddle-wheels were 24 ft. diam., each with 12 fixed radial floats about 8·5 ft. long, and made 15 revs. per min. for a speed of about 9 knots.

Under the command of Lieut. R. Roberts, R.N. (1803-1841), the "Sirius" left London for Cork Harbour, where she coaled, leaving there on the 4th April 1838 with 40 passengers for New York. She encountered strong head-winds, and some of the crew protested, declaring that it was madness to proceed in so small a vessel. However, thanks to the determination and discipline of the commander, the "Sirius" arrived safely off New York on the 22nd April, after an Atlantic crossing of 18 days 10 hrs. at a mean speed of 6·7 knots. She was closely followed by the P.S. "Great Western" (see p. 31) which arrived the next day.

The arrival of the "Sirius" in New York was an occasion of great enthusiasm, reported as follows[59] in one of the local newspapers:—"Nothing is talked of in New York but about this 'Sirius.' She is the first steam vessel that has arrived here from England, and a glorious boat she is. Every merchant in New York went on board her yesterday. Lt. Roberts, R.N., is the first man that ever navigated a steamship from Europe to America." The "Sirius" left New York for her return crossing on the 1st May; at her departure thousands of people assembled on the wharfs, and the Battery saluted with 17 guns, a mark of respect seldom or never before shown to any merchant vessel. She arrived at Falmouth on the 18th May, and proceeded to London the same day. A second double crossing of the Atlantic was completed in July 1838, after which the vessel was used for home and continental services. On one of these trips, between Glasgow and Cork in January 1847, she ran onto a reef of rocks in Ballycotton Bay and became a total wreck.[60]

Principal dimensions of the P.S. "Sirius" were as follows:— Gross register, 703 tons; net, 412 tons; length over all, 208 ft.; length between perps., 178·4 ft.; length of keel, 170 ft.; breadth of hull, 25·8 ft.; breadth over paddle boxes, 47·25 ft.; depth of hold, 18·3 ft.; draught, 15 ft.

P.S. "GREAT WESTERN" (1837)

The first steamer to be constructed for transatlantic service was the "Great Western." She was built of wood at Bristol by Mr. William Patterson, to the plans of Mr. I. K. Brunel, F.R.S. (1806-1859), and launched on the 19th July 1837 for the Great Western Steamship Co. Her first crossing of the Atlantic was accomplished in April 1838, and fully demonstrated the practicability of ocean steamship transport.

To enable the vessel to resist the action of the heavy Atlantic waves, she was constructed with great longitudinal strength. The ribs were of oak, and of scantling equal to that of contemporary line-of-battle ships. They were dowelled and bolted in pairs; there were also four staggered rows of iron bolts, 1·5 in. diam. and 24 ft. long, which ran longitudinally throughout the bottom frames of the ship. She was closely trussed with iron and wooden diagonals and shelf-pieces which, with the whole of her upper works, were fastened with bolts and nuts to a much greater extent than had formerly been the practice. The hull was sheathed with copper below the water-line.

The saloon, which was the principal apartment in the ship, was 75 ft. long, 21 ft. wide, and 9 ft. high, and is stated to have been the largest and most luxurious room provided in any vessel of the period.[61] There was accommodation for 120 first-class passengers and 20 second-class but, if necessary, berths for a further 100 could be provided. The crew consisted of 60 officers and men, so that a total of 300 persons could be accommodated.

The vessel was propelled by side-lever engines of 450 nominal
h.p., constructed by Messrs. Maudslay, Sons and Field, and fitted
in London. There were two cylinders, 73·5 in. diam. by 7 ft. stroke,
which indicated 750 total h.p. Steam at a pressure of 5 lb. per
sq. in. was supplied by four iron return-flue boilers, 11·5 ft. long,
9·5 ft. wide, and 16·75 ft. high, each with three furnaces. The
total heating surface was 3840 sq. ft., and the grate area 202 sq. ft.
These boilers were, however, replaced in 1844 by tubular boilers.
The bunkers provided for 800 tons of coal, but normally not more
than 600 tons were carried. The fuel consumption was about
30 tons per day. The paddle-wheels, which were of the cycloidal
form introduced by Joshua Field in 1833, were 28·75 ft. diam.
with fixed floats 10 ft. long, and made 15 revs. per min.

The "Great Western" was to have sailed from Bristol on the
7th April 1838, but the weather proved unfavourable, and it was
not until the 8th that she left the mouth of the river Avon.[62] She
arrived in New York harbour early on the 23rd April, only a few
hours after the P.S. "Sirius" (see p. 29). The time occupied was
15 days 5 hrs., at a mean speed of 8·8 knots.

The "Great Western" left New York for her return trip on the
7th May, and arrived at Bristol on the 22nd. She continued to
ply between those ports until 1846, and crossed the North Atlantic
64 times in all. In 1847 she was sold to the Royal Mail Steam
Packet Co. Ltd., and ran for ten years[63] in their service between
Southampton and the West Indies. The vessel was broken up
at Vauxhall in 1857.

Principal dimensions of the P.S. "Great Western" were as
follows:—Gross register, 1320 tons; net, 680 tons; length over all,
236 ft.; length between perps., 212 ft.; length of keel, 205 ft.;
moulded breadth, 34 ft.; extreme breadth, 35·3 ft.; breadth over
paddle boxes, 58·3 ft.; depth of hold, 23·2 ft.; mean draught, 16·7 ft.

P.S. "ROYAL WILLIAM" (1837)

Not to be confused with the famous Canadian vessel (see p. 26),
this second paddle steamer of the name was built of wood in 1837
by Messrs. William and Thomas Wilson, of Liverpool, for the Irish
cross-channel service run by the City of Dublin Steam Packet Co.
In 1838 she was chartered by the newly-formed Transatlantic
Steamship Co., and despatched to New York, the smallest vessel

PLATE IV

P.S. "Royal William" (1831), built at Quebec, the first Canadian steamer to cross the Atlantic; first steam vessel to enter the Spanish Navy (see p. 26).

PLATE V

P.S. "Sirius" (1837), the first vessel to cross the
Atlantic under sustained steam power (see p. 29).

that ever steamed the whole distance from Europe to America. This second "Royal William" was constructed of oak and elm with pine planking; all her timbers were treated with corrosive sublimate, to retard their decay. The hull is stated to have been fitted with four transverse water-tight bulkheads of wrought iron.[64] She carried two masts, and was rigged as a topsail schooner. Below deck, she had "capacious accommodation" for 80 passengers.

The vessel was propelled by side-lever engines of 270 nominal h.p., constructed by Messrs. Fawcett and Preston, of Liverpool, with two cylinders 48·5 in. diam. by 66 in. stroke, which developed 400 indicated h.p. Steam was supplied at 5 lb. per sq. in. pressure. The boilers were fired with compressed peat,[65] in addition to coal. The bunkers carried 75 tons of coal, while 365 tons could be stowed in the hold. The paddle-wheels were 24 ft. diam., with fixed radial floats 7 ft. long, and rotated at 16·5 revs. per min. The normal speed of the vessel was about 11 knots, and the fuel consumption 6·25 lb. coal per indicated h.p. per hour.

The "Royal William" was the first steamship to cross the Atlantic from Liverpool, where she left on the 5th July, 1838, with 32 passengers on board. She arrived at New York on the 24th, in 18 days 23 hrs.[66] at a mean speed of 7·3 knots. In all, she made three round trips to New York; then in 1839 she returned to her proper service with the City of Dublin Steam Packet Co. She was later converted into a coal-hulk, and was finally broken up in 1888.

Principal dimensions of the P.S. "Royal William" (1837) were as follows:—Gross register, 617 tons; net, 403 tons; length over all, about 200 ft.; length between perps., 175 ft.; breadth of hull, 27 ft.; breadth over paddle boxes, about 45 ft.; depth of hold, 17·5 ft.; draught, 11 ft.

P.S. "LIVERPOOL" (1837)

The first two-funnel steamer made her appearance on the Atlantic service in 1838. She was built of wood by Messrs. Humble and Milcrest, of Liverpool, and launched on the 14th October, 1837 for Sir John Tobin. Before her completion, however, the vessel was purchased by the newly-formed Transatlantic Steamship Co. for their service between Liverpool and New York.

The "Liverpool" was built of oak and elm, with pine planking, and all the hull timbers were fastened with copper bolts. The frames were trussed with flat iron bar diagonals, placed 8 ft. apart.

Two transverse wrought-iron beams were fitted over each boiler-room, and one over the engine-room. The paddle boxes were cross-braced with iron rods 2·25 in. diam. The vessel carried three masts, and all her fixed rigging was made of copper wire rope. The main saloon was 58 ft. long; there was also another of 45 ft. placed forward. The cabins, most of them double, were fitted with 98 berths. The holds provided for 100 tons of cargo. Four life-boats were carried.

The vessel was propelled by side-lever engines of 468 nominal h.p., constructed by Messrs. G. Forrester and Co., of Liverpool, with two cylinders 75 in. diam. by 7 ft. stroke.[67] Steam at 5 lb. per sq. in. pressure was supplied by four rectangular boilers, two placed forward of the engine-room and two abaft. The bunkers carried 500 tons of coal. The paddle-wheels were 28·5 ft. diam., with fixed radial floats about 9 ft. long, and made about 15 revs. per min.

The "Liverpool" made her first departure from that port on the 20th October 1838, with about 60 passengers, but was forced back into Cork by a violent gale. She left there on the 6th November, and reached New York safely on the 23rd, in 16 days 17 hrs. at a mean speed of 7·9 knots; the coal consumption was 465 tons.[68] In July 1840 the Transatlantic Steamship Co. was wound up; and the vessel was sold, with others, to the Peninsular and Oriental Steam Navigation Co. Ltd. She was increased to 1540 tons, and renamed the "Great Liverpool." She then plied for some time between Southampton, Falmouth and Alexandria, and was wrecked in February 1846 on a reef near Cape Finisterre.

Principal dimensions of the P.S. "Liverpool" were as follows:— Gross register, 1150 tons; net, 560 tons; length over all, 240 ft.; length between perps., 223 ft.; breadth of hull, 30·8 ft.; breadth over paddle boxes, 56 ft.; depth of hold, 21 ft.

P.S. "BRITISH QUEEN" (1838)

Said to have been the most beautiful steamship of her time,[69] the "British Queen" was built of wood by Messrs. Curling and Young, of Limehouse, and launched on the 24th May 1838, for the newly-formed British and American Steam Navigation Co. The vessel was intended to have opened their service between London and New York in April 1838; but she was not completed in time, however, and the P.S. "Sirius" (see p. 29) was therefore chartered by the Company in her stead.

At the time of her launch, the "British Queen" was the largest vessel afloat, and was considered to be the finest achievement of London shipbuilding. Her wooden hull was of very solid construction, braced with iron bolts, and was sheathed with copper to 17 ft. above the keel. She was barque-rigged, with three masts; her figurehead consisted of a representation of H.M. Queen Victoria, beautifully carved and painted white. Accommodation was provided for 207 passengers. The dining saloon was 60 ft. long and 30 ft. wide; there were 104 berths fitted aft, and 103 forward.

The vessel was propelled by side-lever engines of 500 nominal h.p.,[70] with two cylinders 77·5 in. diam. by 7 ft. stroke. These were to have been constructed by Messrs. Claude Girdwood and Co., on the Clyde; but this firm became bankrupt, and the contract was transferred to Robert Napier. Steam was supplied at 5 lb. per sq. in. pressure. The vessel was fitted with a surface condenser,[71] as patented by Samuel Hall in 1834, which enabled her boilers to be fed with pure water. The paddle-wheels were 30 ft. diam., with Galloway floats 9·5 ft. long, and made about 15 revs. per min. The speed of the vessel was 10·2 knots.

The "British Queen" sailed from London on the 10th July 1839, and left Portsmouth for her first Atlantic crossing on the 12th. She carried more than 600 tons of coal, and arrived at New York on the 27th; her mean speed on this occasion was 8·4 knots. In all, she crossed nine times to New York in the service of the British and American Steam Navigation Co. In 1841 she was sold to the Belgian Government, for whom she crossed three times from Antwerp to New York, with an intermediate stop at Cowes. She was broken up in 1842.

Principal dimensions of the P.S. "British Queen" were as follows:—Gross register, 1862 tons; net, 1053 tons; length over all, 275 ft.; length between perps., 245 ft.; length of keel, 223 ft.; breadth of hull, 40·5 ft.; breadth over paddle boxes, 64 ft.; depth of hold, 27 ft.; draught, 17 ft.

P.S. "UNICORN" (1836)

The first vessel owned by the Cunard Line was built of wood by Messrs. Robert Steele and Son, at Greenock, and launched in May 1836 for the service run by Messrs. G. (1795-1890) and J. Burns between Glasgow and Liverpool. She was, however, purchased in 1840 by the newly-formed British and North American Royal Mail Steam Packet Co., which afterwards became the Cunard Steamship Co. Ltd., and sent out to Canada[72] to run between Quebec, Pictou and Halifax, in connection with the transatlantic mail service established by the P.S. "Britannia" (see p. 39) and her three sister-ships.

The "Unicorn" was carvel-built as a three-masted schooner with standing bowsprit, but was later modified as a barque. She had one deck and poop, carried a unicorn head at the bow, and her square stern was decorated with mock quarters. The vessel was propelled by side-lever engines of 274 nominal h.p., constructed by Messrs. Caird and Co. Ltd., at Greenock. These had two cylinders 60 in. diam. by 69 in. stroke,[73] which are said to have developed as much as 560 indicated h.p. Steam at a pressure of 5 lb. per sq. in. was supplied by iron flue boilers, fitted with return elliptical flues, and fed with fresh water. The paddle-wheels were 22·9 ft. diam., each with 21 radial floats 8·4 ft. long and 2·1 ft. wide, and made about 18 revs. per min. for a speed of 8 knots. The normal speed of the vessel in service is said to have been about 9·5 knots.

The "Unicorn" left Liverpool on the 16th May, 1840, under the command of Captain Walter Douglas, with 27 passengers on board. She reached Halifax on the 30th, after 14 days in tempestuous weather,[74] at a mean speed of about 8 knots. With 24 passengers (which included Mr. Edward Cunard), the vessel then proceeded to Boston, where a vociferous reception awaited her arrival on the 2nd June. She is said to have proved herself a "staunch boat" whose machinery worked well.

The "Unicorn" was used by the Cunard Co. to maintain communication between Quebec, Pictou and Halifax; and while on this service in November, 1843, she rescued the survivors of the British sail transport "Premier" (1838), wrecked in the mouth of the St. Lawrence.[75] In 1848 the vessel was refitted with two tubular boilers, 10 ft. long, 10·5 ft. wide and 14 ft. high; each contained 224 brass tubes 3·25 in. internal diam., and three furnaces. She was later sent round to California, where she operated in the Panama and San Francisco trade until about 1853. She then crossed the Pacific to Australia, and was later used between Chinese coast ports and Manila until about 1858.[76]

Principal dimensions of the P.S. "Unicorn" were as follows:—
Gross register, 648 tons; net, 390 tons; length over all, about 185 ft.;
length between perps., 162·9 ft.; breadth of hull, 23·5 ft.; breadth
over paddle boxes, 45·2 ft.; depth of hold, 17·3 ft.

P.S. "PRESIDENT" (1839)

This ill-fated paddle steamer was built of wood by Messrs.
Curling and Young, at Limehouse, and launched on the 7th
December 1839, for the service between London and New York of
the British and American Steam Navigation Co. She was shorter
but rather broader than the P.S. "British Queen" (see p. 34),
launched by the same builders in the previous year.

The "President" was constructed with three decks, the upper
of which was flush from stem to stern. Her timbers were of oak
with fir planking. The transverse frames were solid to the bilge,
and were braced fore-and-aft with iron diagonals. The paddle
boxes rose but little above her deck; and the hull was painted with
gun-ports, like a frigate. She was schooner-rigged, with three
masts, and is said to have presented a very handsome appearance
(see Plate VI). Her accommodation was similar to that of the
"British Queen." The principal saloon was 87 ft. long and 41 ft.
wide in one part. The crew consisted of 80 officers and men.

The vessel was propelled by side-lever engines of 540 nominal
h.p., constructed by Messrs. Fawcett and Preston, of Liverpool,
with two cylinders 80 in. diam. by 7·5 ft. stroke. These were
stated to have been of sound workmanship, but totally inadequate
in power for a vessel of her size; and to this cause her subsequent
misfortunes were mainly attributed. Steam at 5 lb. per sq. in.
pressure was supplied by rectangular flue boilers. The paddle-
wheels were 31 ft. diam.,[77] with Galloway floats 9·25 ft. long, and
made about 15 revs. per min.

The "President" sailed from Liverpool on the 1st August, 1840,
and arrived at New York on the 17th, in 16·5 days at a mean speed
of 8·4 knots. For her second return trip she left New York on
the 11th March, 1841, under the command of Lieut. R. Roberts, R.N.
(see also p. 30). The vessel became overdue; rumours of her safe
arrival were circulated,[78] but it eventually transpired that she had
been lost in a severe Atlantic gale with 136 persons on board.

Principal dimensions of the P.S. "President" were as follows:—
Gross register, 2360 tons; net, about 1350 tons; length over all,

268 ft.; length between perps., 243 ft.; length of keel, 220 ft.; breadth
of hull, 41 ft.; breadth over paddle boxes, 64 ft.; depth from spar-
deck, 32·75 ft.; draught, 17·8 ft. She was the first steam liner to be
lost on the Atlantic. The hazardous aspect of these short-lived
transatlantic steamship companies was dispelled by Mr. Samuel
Cunard, who (as described in the next chapter) laid the foundation
of the Atlantic Steam Ferry.

CHAPTER III

WOODEN MAIL STEAMERS

The advent of steam power across the Atlantic offered a considerable acceleration in the mail service. On her return from New York in 1838, the "Sirius" had overtaken one of the fast mail clippers; the mails were transferred in mid-Atlantic, and the "Sirius" left her far behind.[79] In November 1838, the Admiralty, on behalf of the British Post Office, invited tenders for the transport of H.M. mails to and from Halifax, Nova Scotia; wooden steamers of not less than 300 h.p. were called for, and other conditions were attached.[80]

Two tenders came in response, one from the St. George Steam Packet Co., owners of the "Sirius" (see p. 29), and the other from the Great Western Steamship Co.; but neither complied with the conditions. The British and American Steam Navigation Co. still awaited their first steamer, while those of the Transatlantic Steamship Co. had not proved successful.

The advertisement also reached Mr. Samuel Cunard, in Nova Scotia, and within two weeks, after discussion with his eldest son Edward, he sailed for Falmouth. Cunard was a Scots-Canadian,[81] of natural shrewdness, force of character and experience; already in 1831 he had helped to finance the construction of the pioneer Canadian P.S. "Royal William" (see p. 26). He lost no time, and his offer to the Admiralty was accepted. The first vessel of the Cunard Steamship Co. Ltd. was the P.S. "Unicorn" which, as described in the previous chapter, was purchased in Scotland and sent across to Canada for their local branch service, in anticipation of the Atlantic mail contract.

P.S. "BRITANNIA" (1840)

The paddle steamer "Britannia" was the first vessel built for the British and North American Royal Mail Steam Packet Co., which later became known as the Cunard Steamship Co. Ltd. She was constructed of wood by Messrs. Robert Duncan and Co., at Greenock, and launched on the 5th February 1840. Her three

39

sister-ships, the "Acadia", the "Caledonia" and the "Columbia", were also built on the Clyde about the same time. These four vessels were to establish a monthly transatlantic mail steamship service from Liverpool. to Halifax and Boston, subsidised by the British Post Office. The "Britannia" was the first steamer built to carry the mails between Great Britain and America.

She was a three-masted barque, with two decks, a square stern and clipper bow.[82] On the upper deck, provision was made for the officers' quarters. The total crew consisted of 89 officers and men. There was also a shelter for cows, which were carried in order to ensure supplies of fresh milk. The holds provided for 225 tons of cargo. The passenger accommodation consisted of the dining saloon, and cabins for 115 on the main deck below.[83] This accommodation was described as luxurious; but Charles Dickens (1812-1870), who crossed on the "Britannia" in 1842, placed on record in his *American Notes*[84] a rather depressing account. "Before descending into the bowels of the ship,' he wrote, "we had passed from the deck into a long and narrow apartment, not unlike a gigantic hearse with windows in the sides; having at the upper end a melancholy stove, at which three or four chilly stewards were warming their hands; while on either side, extending down its whole dreary length, was a long, long table; over each of which a rack, fixed to the low roof, and stuck full of drinking-glasses and cruet-stands, hinted dismally at rolling seas and heavy weather."

The vessel was propelled by side-lever engines of 440 nominal h.p., constructed by Robert Napier, with two cylinders, 72 in. diam. by 82 in. stroke, which indicated 740 total h.p. Steam at a pressure of 9 lb. per sq. in. was supplied by four return-flue boilers, each with three furnaces. The total heating surface was 2698 sq. ft., the grate area 222 sq. ft., and the coal consumption about 37 tons per day. The bunkers carried 640 tons. The paddle-wheels were 28 ft. diam.,[85] each with 21 fixed radial floats 8·75 ft. long and 2·8 ft. wide, and made 16 revs. per min. The normal speed of the vessel was about 8·5 knots.

The "Britannia" left Liverpool for her first crossing of the Atlantic, as advertised,[86] on the 4th July, 1840. A contemporary newspaper account states that "the fine vessel is so large that it was necessary to swing her out into mid-stream (the Mersey) and place her passengers aboard from a tender owing to her immense size." She arrived at Halifax in 11 days 4 hrs., at a mean speed of 10 knots, and completed her run to Boston in 14 days 8 hrs. The return crossing was made in a little over ten days; the best steaming was 280 miles in one day. These records entitled her to the Blue Riband of the Atlantic.

In the winter of 1844, when the harbour of Boston was frozen over, the "Britannia" was imprisoned in the ice, and it is recorded that the citizens at their own expense cut a passage, seven miles long and 100 ft. wide, to enable the vessel to reach clear water.[87] The "Britannia" completed 40 crossings of the Atlantic. In 1849 she was sold to the German Government for the purpose of conversion into a warship. Her engines were later removed, and she existed in Germany for several years as a hulk. The vessel was finally broken up at Kiel in 1880-81.

Principal dimensions of the P.S. "Britannia" were as follows:— Gross register, 1156 tons; net, 619 tons; displacement at mean draught, 2050 tons; length over all, 228 ft.; length between perps., 207 ft.; breadth, 34·3 ft.; breadth over paddle boxes, 56 ft.; depth of hold, 22·5 ft.; mean draught, 16·8 ft.

P.S. "CLYDE" (1841)

The Royal West India Mail Co. was founded by Royal Charter in September, 1839, and in March, 1841 entered into a contract with the Admiralty for the conveyance of H.M. mails between this country, the West Indies and the Gulf of Mexico. Fourteen steamships were at once ordered to be built for this contract service, in accordance with Admiralty specifications and under the survey of officers appointed for the purpose.

Of the first batch of four sister-ships, the P.S. "Clyde" was built of wood by Messrs. Robert Duncan and Co., at Greenock, and launched on the 25th February, 1841. She was soon followed by the "Teviot", built by the same firm and launched on the 4th October. The two other vessels were the "Tay" and the "Tweed", built on the Clyde by Messrs. Charles Wood and Co., and Messrs. Thompson and Spiers respectively.

These vessels embodied the "wave-line" principle developed by Mr. John Scott Russell, F.R.S. (1808-1882), and are said to have consisted of the finest class of wooden-built steamship which had been constructed up to that time, and which could readily be made use of in the event of war. Each had two flush decks, with accommodation for 92 passengers, and carried 70 tons of cargo. The crew consisted of 60 officers and men.

The vessels were propelled by side-lever engines of 450 nominal h.p., constructed by Messrs. Caird and Co. Ltd., of Greenock. Each had two cylinders, 74·25 in. diam. by 90 in. stroke; the side-levers were 20 ft. long, and the connecting-rods 16·25 ft. The air pumps were 39 in. diam. by 52 in. stroke. Steam at 10 lb. per sq. in. pressure was supplied by boilers of about 3000 sq. ft. heating surface and 225 sq. ft. grate area. The paddle-wheels were 30 ft. diam., each with 20 fixed radial floats 9·5 ft. long and 2·5 ft. wide,[88] and made 15 revs. per min. The mean speed of the vessels was 7·3 knots, with about 550 indicated h.p., and their coal consumption 26 tons per day.[89] The bunkers carried about 600 tons.

The "Clyde" left Southampton on her maiden trip to the West Indies in December 1841. She was stranded off Nevis in 1842, but was refloated and repaired. Ten years later she was re-boilered and refitted for the inter-Colonial service. In 1865 she was broken up at St. Thomas. The "Teviot" entered service in February 1842; she was sent to the Thames in 1850 for overhaul. In 1851 she was placed on the Brazilian service, and in 1864 was broken up in the West Indies. The "Tweed" was lost with 72 lives[90] on the 12th February 1847, on the Alicranes reefs off Yucatan, in the Gulf of Mexico, while on her way to Vera Cruz.

Principal dimensions of the vessels were as follows:—Gross register, 1354 tons; net, 770 tons; length over all, 238 ft.; length between perps., 213 ft.; breadth of hull, 34·5 ft.; breadth over paddle boxes, about 57 ft.; depth, 24·7 ft.; mean draught, 17·5 ft.

P.S. "HIBERNIA" (1843)

The four pioneer Cunard liners were followed in 1843 by the P.S. "Hibernia," and in 1845 by her sister-ship the "Cambria," both built of wood at Greenock by Messrs. Robert Steele and Son, for the service from Liverpool to Halifax and Boston of the British and North American Royal Mail Steam Packet Co. These vessels were of similar construction to the "Britannia" (see p. 39), but exceeded her in both size and speed.

The "Hibernia" was carvel-built; she carried a female figurehead above her raked clipper bow, and her round stern was decorated with mock quarters. She was at first rigged as a three-masted barque; but her mizzen was removed soon after, and she became a brig. Accommodation for 110 passengers was provided on two decks. For the lower deck, the hull was pierced with 30 portholes on each side, 17 abaft the paddle-wheels and 13 forward. The holds provided for 300 tons of cargo. Four lifeboats were carried.

The vessel was fitted with side-lever engines of 500 nominal h.p., constructed by Robert Napier; these had two cylinders 77·5 in. diam. by 90 in. stroke,[91] which developed a total of 1040 indicated h.p. The paddle-wheels were 31 ft. diam., each with 24 fixed radial floats 9 ft. long and 3 ft. wide, and made about 15 revs. per min. for a speed of 10 knots. Steam at a pressure of 12 lb. per sq. in. was supplied by four iron flue boilers of 3788 sq. ft. total heating surface. These contained 16 furnaces of 247 sq. ft. total grate area, which consumed 48 tons of coal per day. The bunkers provided for 740 tons.

The normal service speed of the "Hibernia" was about 9·25 knots. In 1847, however, she crossed eastward from Halifax to Liverpool in 9 days 1 hr. 30 min., at a mean speed of 11·67 knots, and thereby claimed the Blue Riband of the Atlantic. On the 29th December of that year, she arrived for the first time in New York, and thus marked the extension of the Cunard service to that port. In 1849 she arrived at Boston with a leak, and had to be repaired in New York.[92] In 1850 the "Hibernia" was outclassed; she was sold to the Spanish Government for use as a naval vessel, fitted with new boilers, and renamed the "Habanois." In February 1854, the "Cambria" was taken over by the Admiralty for use as a troopship in the Crimean war.

Principal dimensions of the P.S. "Hibernia" were as follows:— Gross register, 1422 tons; net, 791 tons; displacement, 2580 tons; length over all, about 248 ft.; length between perps., 219 ft.; length of keel, 208 ft.; breadth of hull, 35·8 ft.; breadth over paddle boxes, 58 ft.; depth of hold, 24·2 ft.; mean draught, 17·3 ft.

P.S. "WASHINGTON" (1847)

The first American transatlantic paddle steamer, to follow the "Savannah" (see p. 15), was built of wood by Messrs. Westervelt and Mackay, at New York, and launched on the 31st January 1847 for the service of the newly-formed Ocean Steam Navigation Co. (known as the Bremen Line) between New York, Southampton and Bremen. She was the first vessel of the Line, and was followed in September of the same year by a sister-ship, the "Hermann."

These American steamers were of heavier build than their

D

British contemporaries. The "Washington" was a three-masted barque, constructed with four decks, and painted black with one row of imitation portholes. She had one funnel, and carried a full-length figurehead of her namesake. Accommodation was provided for 120 first and second-class passengers, and the holds carried 300 tons of cargo. The vessel was hailed[93] in New York as the "most complete and beautiful ever constructed," and it was predicted[94] that "she will prove herself an excellent sea boat in all respects." She did, however, prove to be considerably slower than the seven-year-old Cunard "Britannia" (see p. 39), and was described later as one of the ugliest steamships ever put afloat.

The vessel was fitted with side-lever engines of about 550 nominal h.p., constructed by Messrs. Stillman and Allen, at the Novelty Ironworks, New York. These had two cylinders 72 in. diam. by 120 in. stroke,[95] which developed a total of 1100 indicated h.p. Steam at a pressure of about 15 lb. per sq. in. was supplied by two rectangular iron flue boilers, which measured 36 ft. by 15 ft. in plan, and comprised 5944 sq. ft. total heating surface. Each of the boilers had three furnaces 7 ft. long and 4·5 ft. wide, with a total grate area of 189 sq. ft. The flues were 12 in. diam. The coal bunkers carried 600 tons. The paddle-wheels were 34·7 ft. diam., each with 24 fixed radial float boards 7·5 ft. long and 26 in. wide, and are said to have made about 12 revs. per min.[96] for a speed of 11 knots. It is probable, however, that the normal service speed of the vessel did not exceed about 10 knots.

The "Washington" left New York, for her maiden trip, on the 1st June, 1847; and the "Britannia", which left Boston at the same time, beat her by more than two full days. The "Washington" had a cool reception at Southampton, where it was said that she seemed "rather to roll along than steam through the water." In 1851 the two boilers of the "Hermann" were replaced by four of more reasonable size.[97] In 1857 she and the "Washington" were both sold for use in the Pacific, where the latter was broken up in 1863. The "Hermann" was lost on the Japanese coast in February, 1869, with nearly 300 lives.[98]

Principal dimensions of the P.S. "Washington" (1847) were as follows:—Gross register, 1750 tons; displacement, 2680 tons; length over all, 260 ft.; length between perps., 236 ft.; length of keel, 220 ft.; breadth of hull, 39 ft.; breadth over paddle boxes, about 58 ft.; depth of hold, 31 ft.; mean draught, 19·5 ft.

P.S. "UNITED STATES" (1847)

The pioneer vessels of the Bremen Line (see p. 43) were soon followed by another American paddle steamer, named the "United States." She was built of wood in 1847 by William H. Webb, at New York,[99] for Messrs. Charles H. Marshall and Co., who in 1836 had become proprietors of the Black Ball Line of sail packets (see p. 15). The "United States" was used by them in an unsuccessful attempt to start a new steamship service for the same Line between New York and Liverpool.

The vessel was constructed with a flat bottom, which had very little dead rise (about 0·5 in. per foot), in order to provide as much space as possible for the engine-room and coal bunkers.[100] The water-lines at bow and stern were somewhat concave. The sail-packet tradition was otherwise evident in her lines and flare, and in her full deck line forward. The deadwood, keelsons and frames for 50 ft. at each end were of live oak, locust and cedar; the frames were spaced 32 in. apart at the extreme ends. The lower timbers amidships were of southern white oak, spaced 25 in. part; the upper timbers were of live oak, locust and cedar, as at the ends.

The vessel was fitted amidships with five rows of pine keelsons 3 ft. deep, and four rows 16 in. deep. She carried a scroll head and bowsprit above her clipper bow, and had a round stern. The "United States" was built at a three-decked vessel, with three masts, and one funnel forward of the paddle-wheels. Below the main deck were berths for 148 passengers, and hold-space for about 400 tons of cargo. Five lifeboats were carried.

The "United States" was fitted with side-lever engines of about 610 nominal h.p., constructed by Messrs. T. F. Secor and Co., at New York. These had two cylinders 80 in. diam. by 108 in. stroke, and would have developed a total of about 1200 indicated h.p. at sea. Steam at a pressure of about 15 lb. per sq. in. was supplied by boilers placed forward, which consumed about 52 tons of coal per day at full steam. The bunkers carried 800 tons. The paddle-wheels were 35 ft. diam., each with 24 fixed float boards about 8 ft. long, carried on three sets of radial arms. These would have made about 13 revs. per min. for a speed of 10 knots.

Under the command of Captain William G. Hackstaff, the "United States" left New York for her maiden trip on the 8th April, 1848, and arrived at Liverpool on the 22nd,[101] in 13 days 20 hrs., at a mean Atlantic speed of 9·5 knots. The total coal consumption amounted to 520 tons. The vessel is said to have made fair speed with a very moderate horse-power. However, she only completed four round trips for the Black Ball Line, who were unable to run her with profit in the face of competition from the Cunard Steamship Co. Ltd.

In February 1849 the vessel was sold to the German Government for conversion at New York into a warship,[102] for which purpose she was cut down one deck and armed with 12 guns. She could not be delivered, however, until the war with Denmark was over; but she reached Liverpool, en route, on the 16th June.[103] On her arrival in Germany, she was renamed the "Hansa" and stationed on the North Sea coast off Bremen. Three years later, in 1852, she was sold at auction to Messrs. W. A. Fritze und Carl Lehmkuhl, at Bremen, and reconditioned for merchant service between Bremen and New York. This trade proved unprofitable, however, and the vessel was soon withdrawn.

In 1854 the "Hansa" was chartered to the British Admiralty for use as a troopship in the Crimean war. She was also chartered in 1857 to transport British troops to India at the time of the Indian Mutiny. Later she was sold to Mr. John O. Lever, who intended her for service to India, and renamed her the "Indian Empire." The vessel ran her steam trials at Southampton on the 9th June 1858, and is said to have covered the measured nautical mile at a mean speed of 12·55 knots; her paddle-wheels made 16·5 revs. per min.[104]

The "Indian Empire" was then used with the P.S. "Pacific" (see p. 62) and other chartered vessels to promote a new steam service between Ireland and America, later known as the Galway Line (see p. 65), in which Mr. Lever was interested. On her first trip she struck a rock at the entrance to Galway harbour; but, after repairs, she left there on the 19th June[105] with mail for America. In mid-Atlantic, a broken piston rod caused further delay, and it was 12 days before the vessel reached Halifax.

Her second trip was no more fortunate. She left New York on the 23rd October,[106] but came into collision outside the harbour, and had to stop for repairs at Halifax. She left there on the 31st October, and was reported a month later[107] as lost at sea. However, the vessel had in fact battled her way across the Atlantic in tempestuous weather, and had reached Broadhaven on the Irish coast on the 26th November.[108] She is stated to have proved herself "an excellent sea boat" under this ordeal; but with it, however, her Atlantic service came to an end.

The vessel was later sold to Mr. Z. C. Pearson, of Hull, who sent her to London for overhaul. Fire broke out on the 23rd July 1862, while she was anchored in the Thames off Deptford, and this resulted in her complete loss.[109]

Principal dimensions[110] of the P.S. "United States" were as follows:—Gross register, 1858 tons; net, 1087 tons; displacement, 2850 tons; length over all, 268 ft.; length between perps., 244·6 ft.; breadth of hull, 40 ft.; breadth over paddle boxes, about 60 ft.; depth in hold, 30·8 ft.; draught, 18 ft.

P.S. "AMERICA" (1848)

To meet the increased demands of the British transatlantic mail contract, four new Cunard liners were added to the fleet. The P.S. "America" and two of her sister-ships, the "Canada" and the "Niagara," were built of wood in 1848 by Messrs. Robert Steele and Son, of Greenock, for the British and North American Royal Mail Steam Packet Co. Another sister-ship, the "Europa," was built at the same time by Messrs. John Wood (1788-1860) and Co., at Greenock.

These vessels were three-masted barques, similar in construction to their predecessors. Each had accommodation for 140 passengers, and hold-space for 450 tons of cargo. The "America" was described,[111] by one who sailed on her, as follows:—"Her high bulwarks enclosed a series of small cabins ranging alongside the paddle-boxes. On the starboard side were the quarters of the second and third officers and the houses for the butcher, baker, and cow. On the port side were compartments for the purser, surgeon, cook, and ship's stores. Above their roofs were overturned life-boats which sheltered fresh vegetables. In the centre, and near the stern, was the wheel-house. It was raised sufficiently to permit the helmsman to look over the saloon ahead of him. On either side of the wheel-house were cabins for the captain and the first officer. Forward of the saloon was a narrow cross-passage, and then the steward's room with its liquor-dispensing window. Forward of that was the roofed-over capstan space, sheltered and dry under foot. The kitchen, engine-room ventilators, second-class saloon, and sailors' quarters ranged, in that order, forward to the bow. On the unencumbered poop deck above the main saloon, an officer was stationed, at the binnacle, to give orders to the helmsman. This officer, in turn, received instructions from another one stationed at the gangway on the side of the paddle-box where there was a clear view ahead. The officer on post at the gangway could also communicate with the engine-room by pulling a wire which was attached to a bell below decks."

The "America" was fitted with side-lever engines of 670 nominal h.p., constructed by Messrs. Robert Napier and Sons. These had two cylinders 88·5 in. diam. by 96 in. stroke,[112] and developed a total of 1400 indicated h.p. The paddle-wheels were 32 ft. diam., each with 26 fixed radial floats 9 ft. long and 3·2 ft. wide. Steam at 18 lb. per sq. in. pressure was supplied by four iron flue boilers of 4750 sq. ft. total heating surface. These contained 16 furnaces of 300 sq. ft. total grate area, which consumed 60 tons of coal per day. The bunkers carried 840 tons. The normal speed of the vessel was 10 knots.

In her first year of service, the "Europa" crossed from Liverpool to New York in 11 days 3 hrs., at a mean speed of 11·25 knots, and thereby captured the Blue Riband. In February, 1854, she and the "Niagara" were taken over by the Admiralty for use as transports in the Crimean war. The "America" was sold in 1863, converted into a sailer, and renamed "Coalgaconder". In 1866 the "Niagara" was sold, and converted into a sailer for the Australian trade; she was wrecked on the 6th June, 1875, without loss of life. The "Europa" and "Canada" were both sold in 1867; the former was lengthened, and served for some time. The latter was converted into a sailer under the name of "Mississippi", and ran to Mauritius until 1876, when she struck a rock and was condemned. The vessel was repaired, however, and sold to native shipowners in Calcutta, where she was broken up in 1883.

Principal dimensions of the P.S. "America" were as follows:— Gross register, 1825 tons; net, 984 tons; displacement, 3100 tons; length between perps., 251 ft.; breadth of hull, 38 ft.; breadth over paddle boxes, about 61 ft.; depth of hold, 25·3 ft.; mean draught, 17·8 ft.

P.S. "FRANKLIN" (1848)

The pioneer vessel of the New York and Havre Steam Navigation Co.,[113] founded in New York by Messrs. Fox and Livingston, was built of wood in 1848 by Messrs. Westervelt and Mackay. She had

PLATE VI

P.S. "President" (1839), built on the Thames, for service between London and New York; was the first steam liner to be lost on the Atlantic (see p. 37).

PLATE VII

P.S. "Atlantic" (1849), built at New York, first vessel of the unfortunate
Collins Line; two of her sister-ships were lost on the Atlantic (see p. 49).

been intended for the Bremen Line, but was purchased before completion and placed on the Havre Line service between New York, Southampton and Havre. Her companion, the "Humboldt", was launched in 1850 by the same builders.

The vessels were three-masted barques, each with one funnel, and proved faster than those of the Bremen Line (see p. 43). The "Humboldt" had a straight stem without bowsprit, similar to the Collins Line steamers (see p. 50), and a round stern. The hull was painted an unrelieved black. Four lifeboats were carried.

The "Franklin" was fitted with side-lever engines of about 675 nominal h.p., constructed by Messrs. Stillman and Allen, at the Novelty Ironworks, New York. These had two cylinders 93 in. diam. by 96 in. stroke,[114] and developed a total of 1250 indicated h.p. at sea. Four iron flue boilers, placed back to back, supplied steam at about 17 lb. per sq. in. pressure. The paddle-wheels were 32·5 ft. diam., each with 28 radial float boards about 10 ft. long, and would have made about 15 revs. per min. for a speed of 10·5 knots.

The "Franklin" entered service in 1850, and the "Humboldt" in 1851. The normal transatlantic time of these vessels eastwards worked out at 12 days 17 hrs. 9 min., or a mean speed of about 10·5 knots. The "Humboldt" was, however, lost near Halifax harbour on the 6th December, 1853; and the "Franklin" was wrecked at Montauk Point, near New York, also without loss of life, on the 17th July, 1854.

Principal dimensions of the P.S. "Franklin" were as follows:— Gross register, 2184 tons; net, about 1185 tons; length between perps., 263 ft.; breadth of hull, 41·8 ft.; breadth over paddle boxes, about 67 ft.; depth in hold, 26 ft.; mean draught, 18 ft. Those of the P.S. "Humboldt" were:—Gross register, 2350 tons; length between perps., 292 ft.; length of keel, 283 ft.; breadth of hull, 40 ft.; depth in hold, 27 ft.; mean draught, 19 ft.

P.S. "ATLANTIC" (1849)

The unfortunate Collins Line was founded in New York by Mr. Edward K. Collins (1802-1878), and subsidised for the transport of the United States mails. Their first vessel, the P.S. "Atlantic", was built of wood in 1849 by Messrs. William H. Brown, of New York, under the superintendence of Mr. Geo. Steers. With her three sister-ships, the "Pacific", the "Arctic" (1850) and the

"Baltic," she started the first serious competition with British steamers on the fast transatlantic service. The four sister-ships were almost identical, and were so constructed as to be used for war purposes if necessary.

Their hulls were flat-bottomed, built of live oak, planked with pitch pine, braced with lattice-work of iron bars, and fastened with copper bolts. The vessels had three decks (lower, main and spar, with orlop decks fore and aft), were built with rounded sterns, and were notable as the first steamers to have straight stems (see Plate VII). Each carried three masts (the mizzen-mast of the "Baltic" was removed in 1853), and one funnel. There was no bowsprit; the hulls were painted black, with a streak of dark red. The "Atlantic" carried a Triton figurehead, horn in hand, supported on both sides by mermaids. The interior accommodation, for 200 passengers, embodied the latest improvements in ventilation and heating; all the cabins were heated by steam. The crew consisted of 140 officers and men. The holds carried 450 tons of cargo. The lifeboats were made of galvanised iron.

The "Atlantic" was propelled by side-lever engines of 800 nominal h.p., constructed by Messrs. Stillman and Allen, at the Novelty Ironworks, New York. These had two cylinders, 95 in. diam. by 108 in. stroke, which developed a total of 2000 indicated h.p. The condenser air pump was 58 in. diam. by 54 in. stroke. Steam at a pressure of 17 lb. per sq. in. was supplied by four domed rectangular flue boilers. These contained 32 furnaces in pairs, one above the other, with a total grate area of about 495 sq. ft. Each pair of superposed furnaces led into a common rectangular flue, fitted with vertical water-tubes 2 in. diam.[115] The total heating surface was about 16,500 sq. ft. Coal was delivered from the bunkers (about 1000 tons) to the stokeholds by mechanically driven buckets; the daily consumption was 87 tons.

The paddle-wheels were 35·5 ft. diam.,[116] each with 28 radial float boards 11·5 ft. long and 32 in. wide, and made about 15 revs. per min. for a speed of 11·75 knots. At normal draught the wheels dipped 7 ft., with seven paddles immersed.[117]

The "Atlantic" left New York, for her maiden trip, on the 27th April 1850, and arrived at Liverpool on the 10th May. The "Pacific" entered service in September; and in 1851 she crossed from New York to Liverpool in 9 days 20 hrs. 10 min., at a mean speed of 13 knots. The "Baltic" also captured the Blue Riband in 1851, when she crossed from Liverpool to New York in 9 days 18 hrs. at a mean speed of 13·17 knots. The "Arctic" was, however, lost at sea in 1854, and the "Pacific" in 1856. To help restore public confidence, the "Baltic" was fitted with additional water-tight bulkheads;[118] but these disasters and financial difficulties caused the collapse of the Collins Line in 1858.

The "Atlantic" and the "Baltic" were laid up for some time in New York harbour. Early in the Civil War, however, both were purchased for the U.S. Navy and used as troopships.[119] From 1866 to 1870, the vessels served with the short-lived North American Lloyd Co., which ran between New York, Southampton and Bremen. The "Atlantic" was broken up at New York in 1871. The "Baltic" was converted to sail for the wheat trade, but was scrapped at Boston in 1880.

Principal dimensions of the P.S. "Atlantic" were as follows:— Gross register, 2860 tons; net, 1559 tons; displacement, 5200 tons; length over all, 300 ft.; length between perps., 282 ft.; length of keel, 270 ft.; breadth of hull, 45 ft.; breadth over paddle boxes, 73 ft.; depth of hold, 31·4 ft.; mean draught, 19·8 ft.

P.S. "ASIA" (1850)

To meet the American competition of the Collins Line, two new paddle steamers, the "Asia" and the "Africa," were ordered for the British and North American Royal Mail Steam Packet Co. These vessels were built of wood in 1850 by Messrs. Robert Steele and Son, at Greenock. The "Africa" remained on the Atlantic service until 1868, the last wooden vessel in the Cunard fleet.

The vessels were three-masted barques, constructed of the best British oak, and planked double outside and inside. The space between the frames was filled up, from the keel to the gunwale with rock-salt, to preserve the hull from dry rot. Each vessel had accommodation for 160 passengers, and hold-space for 500 tons of cargo. The saloons and berths were said to have lacked "nothing the most refined taste could desiderate."

The "Asia" was propelled by side-lever engines of 816 nominal h.p., constructed by Messrs. Robert Napier and Sons, of Glasgow. These comprised two cylinders, 96 in. diam. by 108 in. stroke, and could develop a total maximum of 2400 indicated h.p.[120] Steam at a pressure of 18 lb. per sq. in. was supplied by four flue boilers of 7032 sq. ft. total heating surface; these contained 20 furnaces

of 417 sq. ft. total grate area. The engine-room crew consisted
of 38 men. At the above maximum horse-power, coal would be
consumed at the rate of about 100 tons per day. The bunkers held
930 tons. The paddle-wheels were 35 ft. diam.,[121] each with 28
fixed radial floats, 9·2 ft. long and 3·2 ft. wide, carried on three
sets of arms, so that eight floats of each wheel were immersed at
normal draught. The speed of the vessel was 12 knots.

In 1850, the "Asia" crossed from Liverpool to Halifax in 8 days
17 hrs., at a mean speed of 12·12 knots, and thereby captured
the Blue Riband. At the time of the Trent crisis, in 1861, she
was chartered by the Admiralty as a troopship to Canada. Her
last trip for the Cunard Line was made in 1867, after which she
was sold and converted to sail; the hull was burned at Bombay in
1878. The "Africa" was reboilered in 1857. She was used by
the Government in 1867 as a floating barracks at Liverpool, and
was sold out of the Cunard service in 1868.

Principal dimensions of the P.S. "Asia" were as follows:—Gross
register, 2226 tons; net, 1214 tons; displacement, 3620 tons; length
over all, 290 ft.; length between perps., 266 ft.; breadth of hull,
40 ft.; breadth over paddle boxes, 63 ft.; depth of hold, 27·2 ft.;
mean draught, 18·8 ft.

P.S. "ARABIA" (1852)

The last vessel to be built of wood for the Cunard Steamship
Co. Ltd., was the P.S. "Arabia". Her keel was laid at Greenock
in 1850, by Messrs. Robert Steele and Son, before the full measure
of the Collins Line competition was realised. She appeared on the
Atlantic in 1852.

The "Arabia" was a two-masted vessel with two funnels. The
lines of the hull were expectionally fine forward; the vessel proved
fast in smooth water, but very "wet" in rough weather. She had
accommodation for 180 passengers and hold space for about
750 tons of cargo. Six lifeboats were carried.

The vessel was propelled by side-lever engines of 938 nominal
h.p.,[122] constructed by Messrs. Robert Napier and Sons, at Glasgow.
These had two cylinders, 103 in. diam. by 108 in. stroke, and
developed 2830 indicated h.p. Steam at a pressure of about
18 lb. per sq. in. was supplied by four tubular box boilers, of
16,948 sq. ft. total heating surface. These boilers (said to have been
the largest of their kind constructed to date) were taken on board in

sections, after the launch, and riveted up inside the vessel. The tubes were horizontal and ran athwartships; the furnaces faced one another. There were 24 furnaces, of 642 sq. ft. total grate area, which consumed 120 tons of coal per day. The bunkers carried 1400 tons. The paddle-wheels were 35·5 ft. diam.,[123] each with 28 fixed radial floats 10·5 ft. long and 3·2 ft. wide, and made 15·5 revs. per min. The normal speed of the vessel was 12·5 knots. In the Crimean war she was used to transport French troops from Marseilles to the Black Sea. In 1864 she was sold out of the service as uneconomical, and converted into a sailing vessel.

Principal dimensions of the P.S. "Arabia" were as follows:— Gross register, 2402 tons; net, 1474 tons; displacement, 3950 tons; length over all, about 309 ft.; length between perps., 285 ft.; breadth of hull, 40·7 ft.; breadth over paddle boxes, 66·5 ft.; depth of hold, 27·6 ft.; mean draught, 19 ft.

P.S. "NORTH STAR" (1853)

This remarkable two-funnel vessel was built in 1853 as a private steam yacht for Commodore Cornelius Vanderbilt (1794-1877).[124] Her wooden hull was constructed at New York by Jeremiah Simonson; and such were her proportions that she was later run by Vanderbilt as one of the liners in his transatlantic service between New York, Southampton and Havre.

The "North Star" was a two-masted brigantine, with two slender funnels. Her hull frames were spaced 2 ft. apart, and four of them were filled in solid to form transverse water-tight bulkheads. She had a straight vertical stem without bowsprit, and the usual rounded stern. As an Atlantic liner, the "North Star" was able to accommodate about 250 passengers. Four lifeboats were carried.

The vessel was propelled by overhead beam engines of about 420 nominal h.p., constructed by Messrs. Secor and Braisted, at the Allaire Works, New York. These had two vertical cylinders 66 in. diam. by 120 in. stroke, which developed a total of about 1250 indicated h.p. Steam at 20 lb. per sq. in. maximum and about 18 lb. per sq. in. normal pressure was supplied by four iron boilers 23·9 ft. long, 11 ft. wide and 10·5 ft. high, of 4892 sq. ft. total heating surface,[125] and with 12 furnaces of about 210 sq. ft. total grate area. Two of the boilers were placed forward, and two abaft the engine-room. The fire-bars were 7·2 ft. long. Anthracite coal was used, of which 600 tons were carried in the bunkers.

The paddle-wheels were 33 ft. diam., each with 28 fixed radial floats 8 ft. long and 18 in. wide. These dipped 7·8 ft., and turned at 16 revs. per min. for a normal speed of about 10 knots. It is said that when Vanderbilt cruised to Europe[126] on the "North Star" in 1853-54, the vessel was so impressive that no one could believe that its owner was merely a private citizen.

Later in 1855, the vessel was refitted for the new Vanderbilt Line,[127] and left New York on the 21st April for Southampton and Havre.[128] She did not, however, prove successful on the Atlantic, and was later chartered for the American Civil War. In 1865 she was taken over by the Pacific Mail Steamship Co., and in October she nearly foundered off Cape Hatteras. After her return to New York, the "North Star" was found to be in such bad condition that she was condemned, and broken up in 1866 at New London, Connecticut.

Principal dimensions of the P.S. "North Star" were as follows:— Gross register, 2000 tons; displacement, about 3150 tons; length between perps., 269 ft.; breadth of hull, 38 ft.; breadth over paddle boxes, about 59 ft.; depth in hold, 29·5 ft.; draught, 19 ft.

P.S. "ARIEL" (1855)

To run as a companion with the "North Star" on his transatlantic service, Commodore Cornelius Vanderbilt ordered the P.S. "Ariel," which was built of wood at New York by Jeremiah Simonson, and launched on the 3rd March 1855. The intention was to maintain a service every three weeks with these two steamers[129] between New York, Southampton and Havre.

The "Ariel" was a two-masted fore-topsail schooner with one funnel. The wooden hull was strapped with diagonal and double-laid iron braces. Like her companion, she had a straight vertical stem without bowsprit, and a rounded stern. Her engine beam rose prominently above decks, between the paddle boxes. Accommodation is said[130] to have been provided for 284 passengers; the state-rooms were furnished with Thompson life-preserving seats.[131] Four lifeboats were carried.

The vessel was propelled by an overhead beam engine of about 300 nominal h.p., constructed by Messrs. Secor and Braisted, at the Allaire Works, New York. There was one vertical cylinder 75 in. diam. by 132 in. stroke,[132] which could no doubt have developed about 900 indicated h.p. Steam at about 18 lb. per sq. in. pressure was supplied by two return-flue boilers 32 ft. long, 12·5 ft. wide and 11·7 ft. high, with about 3700 sq. ft. total heating surface. Each boiler contained three furnaces, with fire-bars 7·5 ft. long. The total grate area was about 125 sq. ft., and the coal consumption 38 tons per day under natural draught. The funnel was 74 in. diam. and 48 ft. high. The coal bunkers carried 600 tons. The paddle-wheels were 33 ft. diam., each with 28 fixed radial floats 8 ft. long and 18 in. wide. The normal speed of the vessel was about 10 knots.

The "Ariel" left New York on the 20th May 1855 for Southampton and Havre, under the command of Captain Peter C. Lefebvre,[133] who was later transferred to the P.S. "Vanderbilt" (see p. 56). She continued on this service, with interruptions, until 1859. In the American Civil War she was chartered by the United States Navy for the transport of troops and supplies.

After the war she was laid up for some time, then taken over in 1868 and used in an attempt to start another transatlantic line which ended in failure. Later in the same year she was sold to the Pacific Mail Steamship Co., and transferred to the Far East. In 1873 she ran between Yokohama and Hakodate; and on the 27th October she struck a reef at Honshu, about 100 miles from Yokohama, and sank in 20 min., but without loss of life.[134]

Principal dimensions of the P.S. "Ariel" were as follows:— Gross register, 1736 tons; displacement, about 2700 tons; length between perps., 252 ft.; breadth of hull, 33·5 ft.; breadth over paddle boxes, about 54 ft.; depth to spar-deck, 26 ft.; draught, 19 ft.

P.S. "ARAGO" (1855)

To replace their lost "Humboldt" and "Franklin" (see p. 48), the New York and Havre Steam Navigation Co. ordered two new vessels. The first of these was the P.S. "Arago," built of wood by Messrs. Westervelt and Mackay, of New York,[135] and launched in June 1855. Her sister-ship, the "Fulton," was built by Messrs. Smith and Dimon, also at New York, under the superintendence of Captain William Skiddy, and launched in February 1856.

These vessels were two-masted brigs, each with two funnels, and constructed with three decks. The stems were almost straight, had a small rake forward, but carried no bowsprit. The sterns were rounded. On the berth-deck, accommodation was provided for 150 first and second-class passengers, and it was said that

300 could be carried. The holds provided for 700 tons of cargo. Each vessel carried two wooden lifeboats forward of the paddle-wheels, and six Francis metallic lifeboats aft.[136]

The machinery for these vessels consisted in each case of two inclined oscillating cylinders 65 in. diam. by 120 in. stroke.[137] These were constructed by Messrs. Stillman and Allen, of New York, and inclined 24 deg. from the vertical[138] at mid-oscillation in the case of the "Arago", which developed about 1860 indicated h.p. The cylinders on the "Fulton" were fitted by the Morgan Iron Works, at New York, and were inclined 45 deg. to the vertical at mid-oscillation. Steam at a pressure of about 18 lb. per sq. in. was supplied by two iron Martin boilers, 12 ft. long and 30 ft. wide, one placed forward and one abaft the engine-room. These had vertical seamless brass water-tubes, drawn from ingots by the American Tube Co.; the total heating surface amounted to 9100 sq. ft. The daily coal consumption was about 75 tons; the bunkers carried 800 tons. The paddle-wheels were 31 ft. diam, each with 28 radial floats 9 ft. long and 18 in. wide, and made about 16 revs. per min. for a speed of 10·5 knots.

In 1858 the "Fulton" left New York on the 18th September, and arrived at Southampton on the 1st October, at a mean speed of 10·2 knots.[139] These vessels continued on the Havre Line service without much incident until 1861, when both were chartered by the U.S. Government as transports in the Civil War, and the Line was withdrawn. The "Arago" was later sold to the Peruvian Government; but the hull of the "Fulton" had become rotten and had to be broken up. Her engines were, however, taken out and utilised in another vessel.

Principal dimensions of the vessels were as follows:—Gross register, 2300 tons; displacement, 3000 tons; length on deck, 290 ft.; length between perps, 280·5 ft.; breadth of hull, 42·3 ft.; breadth over paddle boxes, 65·5 ft.; depth of hold, 24 ft.; mean draught, 17·5 ft.

P.S. "VANDERBILT" (1855)

This fast Atlantic paddle steamer was built of wood by Jeremiah Simonson, of New York, for his uncle, Commodore Cornelius Vanderbilt, and launched on the 17th December, 1855.[140] The vessel was used on the Vanderbilt Line service between New York, Southampton and Havre.

The "Vanderbilt" was a two-masted brig with two funnels. The bottom was nearly flat, built of solid white oak timbers, 15 in. by 21 in., bolted together lengthwise of the ship. The iron bolts were 1·25 in. diam. and 7 ft. long. The frames, also of white oak, were closely spaced, and fastened with diagonal wrought-iron straps. The oak planking of the hull was 6 in. thick, and was coppered below the water-line.[141] The stem was straight and vertical without bowsprit; the stern was rounded. Accommodation is said to have been provided for about 370 passengers. Six lifeboats were carried.

The vessel was propelled by overhead beam engines of about 950 nominal h.p., constructed by Messrs. Secor and Braisted, at the Allaire Works, New York. These had two vertical cylinders 90 in. diam. by 144 in. stroke,[142] which developed a total of 2800 indicated h.p. The beams rose above the paddle boxes, and must have attracted considerable attention. Steam at a pressure of 18 lb. per sq. in. was supplied by four tubular boilers, 28 ft. long, 13 ft. wide and 14 ft. high, of 20,000 sq. ft. total heating surface, and fired from the side. The daily coal consumption would be about 112 tons; the bunkers carried 1400 tons.[143] Two of the boilers were placed forward, and two abaft the engine-room. The two funnels, one to each pair, were 11 ft. diam. The paddle-wheels were of wrought iron, 42 ft. diam., each with three flanges, and radial floats 11 ft. long, and made about 15 revs. per min. for a speed of 13 knots.

The "Vanderbilt" entered service in 1857; and in May, 1859, under the command of Captain Peter C. Lefebvre, from the "Ariel" (see p. 54), she made a record trip from the Needles to New York, a distance of 3115 nautical miles, in 9 days 9 hrs. 26 min.,[144] at a mean speed of 13·8 knots. She continued on the New York, Southampton and Havre route until November, 1860; but on the outbreak of the Civil War in 1861, Commodore Vanderbilt presented her to the U.S. Government, and she was armed as a cruiser. Afterwards she was laid up for some time, until sold at Mare Island Navy Yard in March, 1873 to Messrs. Howes Bros. Her engines were removed and she was converted[145] into the well-known three-masted clipper, "Three Brothers". In 1885 she was sold to the Anchor Line, for use as a coal hulk at Gibraltar; and in September 1930 she was sold to the shipbreakers.

Principal dimensions of the P.S. "Vanderbilt" were as follows:—

E

Gross register, 3360 tons;[146] displacement, 5270 tons; length over all, 335 ft.; length between perps., 328 ft.; breadth of hull, 47·5 ft.; breadth over paddle boxes, 74 ft.; depth of hold, 31·1 ft.; mean draught, 19·6 ft.

P.S. "ADRIATIC" (1856)

The last wooden paddle steamer to be built for transatlantic service was the "Adriatic." The hull was constructed at New York, by Mr. Geo. Steers, and launched on the 8th April 1856. This vessel was intended to retrieve the fortunes of the unsuccessful Collins Line, subsidised for the transport of United States mails between New York and Liverpool.

The hull was divided by seven transverse bulkheads into separate water-tight compartments, and was constructed with a straight vertical stem and a round stern. The spar-deck, 20 ft. above the water-line, was flush from stem to stern. The vessel had two funnels and two masts, but no bowsprit. She was fitted with 130 ventilated and steam-heated cabins, for 316 first-class and 60 second-class passengers.[147] The main dining-saloon measured 75 ft. long and 28 ft. wide, and could seat 200 at one meal. The crew of the vessel consisted of 170 officers and men. She carried 16 metallic lifeboats, each to accommodate 60 persons.[148] The holds provided space for 800 tons of cargo.

The machinery of the "Adriatic" was constructed by Messrs. Stillman and Allen, at the Novelty Ironworks, New York, and was rated at 1300 nominal h.p. It comprised two oscillating cylinders, 101 in. diam. by 144 in. stroke, which both worked onto the same crank-pin, and developed a total of about 3600 indicated h.p. In the first instance, a new form of part-rotary valve, invented by Mr. H. Allen, was fitted; but this proved troublesome on trial, and so the usual double poppet valves were later substituted.[149] The air pump was 42 in. diam. by 60 in. stroke.

Steam at a pressure of 20 lb. per sq. in. was supplied by eight tubular boilers, 20·1 ft. long, 11·25 ft. wide and 14 ft. high, four placed forward of the engine-room and four abaft. The vertical brass water-tubes were 2 in. outside diam., and the total heating surface 30,758 sq. ft. Each boiler contained six furnaces, placed side by side; the total grate area was 1260 sq. ft., and the daily coal consumption about 145 tons. The bunkers carried 1200 tons. The two funnels were 7 ft. diam. and 40 ft. high. The paddle-wheels were 40 ft. diam.,[150] each with 32 fixed radial float boards 12 ft. long and 3 ft. wide, and made 13 revs. per min. for a speed of 13 knots.

The "Adriatic" left New York for her maiden trip on the 23rd November 1857; she reached Liverpool in ten days, at a mean speed of about 13 knots, and returned to New York. On the failure of the Collins Line in 1858, the vessel remained for some time laid up in New York. She was purchased in 1861 by the Atlantic Royal Mail Steam Navigation Co., known as the Galway Line, and was the only vessel in their service able to maintain the mail contract speed. She crossed from Galway to St. John's, Newfoundland, in six days, and returned in the record time of 5 days 19 hrs. 45 min. When the Galway Line failed in 1864, the "Adriatic" was sold, and converted to sail in the San Francisco trade. She was later sold to the African Steam Ship Co. for use as a store-ship, and sent out to Bonny, on the West African coast. In 1885 she had to be hurriedly beached, and was found to be beyond repair.

Principal dimensions[151] of the P.S. "Adriatic" were as follows:— Gross register, 3670 tons; net, about 2100 tons; displacement, 5890 tons; length over all, 351·7 ft.; length between perps., 343·8 ft.; length of keel, 330 ft.; breadth of hull, 50 ft.; breadth over paddle boxes, about 79 ft.; depth in hold, 32·8 ft.; mean draught, 20 ft. She was the last paddle steamer ever built of wood for the Atlantic mail service. The staunch old "wooden walls" had served their time, but (as described in the next chapter) could not stem the advance of iron hull construction.

CHAPTER IV

IRON AND STEEL SHIPS

In this last phase of Atlantic paddle steamers, the timber suitable for ship construction had become scarce and expensive, and naval architects were forced to consider the use of iron. At first, this innovation met with serious opposition; many experienced ship-builders declared that to build vessels of a heavy metal was "contrary to nature." An iron boat is said to have been made as early as 1787 by John Wilkinson (1728-1808) at Willey. In 1818 a small vessel, the "Vulcan", was built of iron by Thomas Wilson (1781-1873) at Faskine, Scotland, for canal use.

The first iron paddle steamer was the "Aaron Manby", built at the Horseley Ironworks, Tipton, and assembled at London in 1822.[152] Public confidence in the seaworthiness of iron ships was, however, finally established by the P.S. "Garry Owen", a vessel of 263 tons, built in 1834 by John Laird (1805-1874), later Messrs. Laird Bros., at Birkenhead.

The first steamer to be built of steel was the paddle launch "Ma Robert", used in 1858 by Dr. David Livingstone (1813-1873) for his expedition up the river Zambesi.[153] The steel hull of 13 tons displacement was built by Messrs. Laird Bros., and fitted with machinery of 12 nominal h.p. which earned for it the nick-name "Asthmatic". Steel manufacture on an adequate scale for ocean liners, however, came too late for the paddle-wheel. Some small paddlers were built of steel[154] as blockade-runners in the American Civil War; but, so far at least as the Atlantic mail service was concerned, paddle steamers ended with iron.

P.S. "PERSIA" (1855)

The first iron vessel of the Cunard Steamship Co. Ltd., and the first iron paddle steamer on the Atlantic, was the P.S. "Persia", built in 1855 by Messrs. Robert Napier and Sons, at Glasgow, the firm which had constructed machinery for so many earlier steamers of the Cunard Line.

The "Persia" was a two-masted vessel, with two funnels. Her keel was built up of iron bars, 13 in. deep and 4·5 in. thick, in sections of about 35 ft., scarfed and riveted. The keel-plates were 0·69 in. thick. The iron sternpost was 13 in. wide and 5 in. thick, and carried the rudder on a spindle 8 in. diam. The frames were spaced 10 in. apart; the ribs were 10 in. deep, with double angle-irons at the outer and inner edges. The hull plates were laid alternately, to ensure continuous longitudinal strength. The bottom plates were 0·94 in. thick; up to the load water-line the plates were 0·75 in. thick; and above, 0·69 in. thick. The plates around the gunwales were 0·88 in. thick.

The hull was subdivided internally into seven water-tight compartments. The holds were placed down the centre of the vessel, with the coal bunkers on either side, and a double bottom beneath. The hold-spaces, for 1100 tons of cargo,[155] were made water-tight and, in the event of accident to the hull, would suffice to keep the ship afloat. Accommodation was provided for 250 passengers; eight lifeboats were carried.

The "Persia" was fitted with side-lever engines of 950 nominal h.p., constructed by the hull builders, with two cylinders 100·5 in. diam. by 120 in. stroke,[156] which developed 3600 indicated h.p. The paddle-wheels were 38 ft. diam., each with 30 fixed radial floats 10·5 ft. long and 3 ft. wide, and made about 17 revs. per min. Steam at 20 lb. per sq. in. pressure was supplied by eight tubular box boilers of 26,080 sq. ft. total heating surface. These contained 40 furnaces, of 800 sq. ft. total grate area, which consumed about 143 tons of coal per day. The bunkers carried 1640 tons. The normal speed of the vessel was 13 knots.

In July, 1856 she crossed from Liverpool to New York in 9 days 1 hr. 45 min., at a mean speed of 13·82 knots, and thereby claimed the Blue Riband, which she held until 1862. At the time of the Trent crisis, in 1861, she was commissioned by the Admiralty as a troopship to Canada. The "Persia" was sold out of the Cunard service in 1868, and broken up on the Thames in the early seventies.[157]

Principal dimensions[158] of the P.S. "Persia" were as follows:—Gross register, 3300 tons; net, 2079 tons; displacement, about 5850 tons; length over all, 398 ft.; length between perps., 376 ft.; length of keel, 350 ft.; breadth of hull, 45·3 ft.; breadth over paddle boxes, 71 ft.; depth of hold, 29·8 ft.; mean draught, 20 ft.

P.S. "PACIFIC" (1854)

This mail paddle steamer was built of iron by Messrs. John Scott Russell and Co., at Millwall, and launched[159] on the 23rd September 1854 for the Sydney and Melbourne Steamship Co. She embodied the "wave-line" principle developed by Mr. Russell, and was intended at the time to be the fastest steamer in the world. In October 1858 she was chartered by the promoters of a new Atlantic Royal Mail Steam Navigation Co., later known as the Galway Line (see p. 65), and sent out to St. John's, Newfoundland. She arrived there on the 21st October, and returned to Galway in six days.[160]

The hull was built on the longitudinal method, with "wave-line" bow and stern, and only a few feet of parallel middle body. The vessel had a clipper stem and round stern, and was subdivided internally into nine water-tight compartments. Her plating rose to the top of the gunwale, and was continuous with the interior skin of the paddle boxes, in order to strengthen the centre of the hull. Her sponsons were provided with open gratings to diminish the surface exposed to wave impact. Accommodation was provided for 80 first-class and 165 second-class passengers, and for a certain amount of cargo.

The vessel was propelled by oscillating condensing engines of 450 nominal h.p., constructed by Messrs. John Scott Russell and Co., with two cylinders 74 in. diam. by 7 ft. stroke, which indicated 1680 h.p. Steam at a pressure of 18 lb. per sq. in. was supplied by four box boilers, 14·8 ft. long, 18 ft. wide and 12·5 ft. high, each with five furnaces, and 440 return tubes 6 ft. long and 3 in. diam. The total heating surface was 9507 sq. ft., and the grate area 420 sq. ft. The consumption of coal was about 2·8 tons per hour. The paddle-wheels were 27 ft. diam.; each had 14 feathering floats 10 ft. long and 4 ft. wide. The vessel had two funnels, and two masts with a sail area of 883 sq. yds. Her mean speed was 14 knots. The "Pacific" was sold to Messrs. Fraser, Trenholm and Co. in December 1861, for use as a blockade-runner. In 1874 she foundered off Cape Flattery with heavy loss of life.

Principal dimensions of the P.S. "Pacific" were as follows:— Gross register, 1469 tons; net, 985 tons; length over all, 270 ft.; length between perps., 255 ft.; length on load water-line, 245·2 ft.; breadth of hull, 32·1 ft.; breadth over paddle boxes, 54 ft.; depth, 18 ft.; mean draught, 12 ft.

P.S.S. "GREAT EASTERN" (1858)

We now come to the most ambitious failure in the whole history of naval architecture: a premature leviathan conceived and built 40 years in advance of practical experience. About 1852, Mr. Isambard K. Brunel, F.R.S., proposed to the Eastern Steam Navigation Co. the construction of a steamship for the Indian and Australian trade, to be five or six times the size of any then in use. It was well known that large vessels possessed great advantages over small ones for long distances; and that the greater the ship, the higher would be the speed. It was estimated that a vessel of the dimensions proposed for the "Leviathan" would maintain a speed of 15 knots, with less power per ton than ordinary vessels required at 10 knots. The size would also provide superior passenger accommodation and cargo space, with a fuel endurance that would render coaling abroad unnecessary. Mr. Brunel also proposed the use of both paddle-wheels and screw propulsion;[161] and in this respect the so-called "Leviathan" was to be unique in transatlantic history.

The construction of such a vessel was decided upon, and arrangements were made with Messrs. John Scott Russell and Co., of Millwall, to build the hull. The first plates of the great ship were laid on the 1st May 1854. Instead of the usual keel, there was a flat plate of iron, 2 ft. wide and 1 in. thick, which ran from stem to stern of the vessel.[162] The form of the hull followed the lines that had for many years been adopted by Mr. John Scott Russell F.R.S., in his "wave-line" principle;[163] and she was built with 120 ft. of parallel middle body. Mr. Brunel, however, proposed the cellular construction of the hull. This was double from the keel to the water-line; the distance between the inner and outer skins was 2·8 ft., and this was rendered cellular by horizontal webs of iron, spaced 6 ft. apart. The vessel had four decks, and all her frames were longitudinal.[164]

The hull was divided transversely by iron bulkheads into ten separate water-tight compartments, each 60 ft. long, through which there was no opening whatever below the second deck. Two longitudinal bulkheads, 36 ft. apart, traversed 350 ft. of the length of the ship. Besides these, there was in each compartment a second intermediate bulkhead, which formed a coal bunker, and was carried up to the main deck. At the bow and stern were additional bulkheads. Two continuous tunnels ran through the principal bulkheads, near the water-line, along one of which the steam pipes passed. The main deck was double or cellular, and this also contributed to the longitudinal strength of the hull. The vessel had five funnels 6 ft. diam., and six masts (see Plate VIII) which spread 6500 sq. yds. of canvas. Accommodation was provided for 800 first-class, 2000 second-class, and 1200 third-class passengers. As a troopship, the vessel could have carried 10,000 men. The total crew consisted of 400 officers and men; and 20 lifeboats were carried. The holds provided for 6000 tons of cargo.

Three months after the first attempt, the vessel was launched sideways[165] into the Thames, under the name of "Great Eastern", on the 31st January, 1858. She weighed at the time 12,000 tons, and rested in two cradles, each 80 ft. square, which were to slide on inclines 80 ft. wide and 200 ft. long, set at a slope of 1 in 14. After starting a few feet, however, the inclines failed, and the vessel was subsequently moved slowly into the water by the application of extensive hydraulic machinery. These troubles caused financial difficulties, which stopped further work, so that it was only in September, 1859 that the trial trip took place.

The enormous paddle-wheels, as first built, were 56 ft. diam.,[166] each with 30 fixed radial floats 13 ft. long and 3 ft. wide. These were driven by engines of 1000 nominal h.p., constructed by Messrs. John Scott Russell and Co., with four oscillating cylinders 74 in. diam. by 14-ft. stroke, which developed 3410 indicated h.p. at 10·75 revs. per min.[167] Steam was supplied at 24 lb. per sq. in. pressure, by four double-ended tubular boilers of the rectangular or box pattern, 17·5 ft. long, 17·8 ft. wide and 13·8 ft. high, with a total heating surface of 19,200 sq. ft. Each boiler contained ten furnaces, and the total grate area of the 40 furnaces amounted to 960 sq. ft.[168] Propelled by her paddle-wheels alone, the "Great Eastern" attained a speed of 7·25 knots.

Her screw propeller was of cast iron, four-bladed, 24 ft. diam. and 37 ft. pitch. It was driven by engines of 1600 nominal h.p., constructed by Messrs. James Watt and Co., of Birmingham, with four horizontal direct-acting cylinders 84 in. diam, by 48-in. stroke, which indicated 4890 total h.p. at 38·8 revs. per min. Steam to these screw engines was supplied at 25 lb. per sq. in. pressure by six double-ended tubular boilers, 18·5 ft. long, 17·5 ft. wide and 14 ft. high, with a total heating surface of 30,000 sq. ft. Each boiler had 12 furnaces, and the total grate area of the 72 furnaces

PLATE VIII

P.S.S. "Great Eastern" (1858), the leviathan of the nineteenth century, with both paddle-wheels and a screw propeller; built on the Thames (see p. 63).

PLATE IX

P.S. "Scotia" (1861), built of iron by Napier, last and finest paddle steamer of the Cunard Line; remained on the Atlantic service until 1875 (see p. 67).

amounted to 1368 sq. ft. The coal bunkers carried 12,000 tons. On a trial of the ship with screw propulsion alone, a speed of 9 knots was obtained.

The "Great Eastern" left Southampton on the 17th June 1860, for her first trip to New York, where she arrived on the 28th; her mean speed on this occasion was 14 knots, and the coal consumption 12·5 tons per hour. Her normal coal consumption was at the rate of 330 tons per day. At the time of the Trent crisis, in June 1861, the "Great Eastern" was chartered as a troopship, and carried 2125 men to Canada. Later, in September, she encountered a severe Atlantic storm, and her paddle-wheels had to be replaced with new ones 50 ft. diam.[169] Due mainly to the relatively small power of her engines, and to her consequent low speed, the ship was never a commercial success either as a passenger or cargo steamer. Her most valuable work was done between 1865 and 1873, when she laid a number of transatlantic cables for the Telegraph Construction and Maintenance Co., an application for which her great size rendered her specially suitable. After this she did no more useful work. In 1888 she was sold as old metal, and was broken up in the course of the three subsequent years.[170] Not until 1899 was she exceeded in size.

Principal dimensions of the P.S.S. "Great Eastern" were as follows:—Gross register, 18,915 tons; net, 13,344 tons; displacement, 32,000 tons; length on upper deck, 692 ft.; length between perps., 680 ft.; length of keel, 630 ft.; breadth of hull, 82·7 ft.; breadth over paddle boxes, 118 ft.; depth of hold, 48·2 ft.; draught, 30 ft.

P.S. "CONNAUGHT" (1860)

The short-lived Atlantic Royal Mail Steam Navigation Co., known as the Galway Line, was formed in 1859 under contract with the British Post Office, for the transport of H.M. mails to Boston and New York via Galway and St. John's, Newfoundland; and four new paddle steamers were ordered for the service. The first of these was the P.S. "Connaught," built of iron at Newcastle, and launched on the 21st April 1860 from the yards of Palmers Shipbuilding and Iron Co. Ltd., who also built the "Hibernia." The two other sister-ships, the "Anglia" and "Columbia," were built in the same year by Messrs. Martin Samuelson and Co., at Hull.

The iron hull of the "Connaught" was subdivided by transverse bulkheads into seven water-tight compartments, and it was stated[171] that should 40 ft. of her bow be carried away in collision, she would still float on an even keel. The vessel had a spar-deck, straight stem and elliptical stern, and was built on the "wave-line" principle, to lines, plans and specifications approved by the Admiralty. She had two masts and two funnels. The hull plates were double-riveted, and in some places treble-riveted. The state-rooms, for 467 passengers, were said to have been comfortable and convenient; the main first-class saloon was 122 ft. long. The crew consisted of 124 officers and men.

The machinery of this vessel, and of her sister the "Hibernia," was of 800 nominal h.p., and comprised three oscillating cylinders 80 in. diam. by 96 in. stroke. That of the "Anglia" and the "Columbia," also of 800 nominal h.p., comprised two oscillating cylinders 98 in. diam. by 96 in. stroke, and developed 3200 indicated h.p. on trial.[172] The cylinders for the air pumps were 34 in. diam. Steam at a pressure of 23 lb. per sq. in. was supplied by eight tubular boilers with a total of 20,000 sq. ft. heating surface.[173] These were fitted with superheaters, and each had five furnaces; the total grate area was 800 sq. ft. The coal consumption was about 125 tons per day; the bunkers carried 1200 tons. The paddle-wheels were 34 ft. diam., fitted with feathering floats 12 ft. long and 4·7 ft. wide, and made about 17 revs. per min. for a speed of 13 knots.

The Galway service was due to commence in June 1860; but it was not until the 11th July that the "Connaught" left Galway. She did not call at St. John's, and arrived 22 hrs. 30 min. late at Boston. On her second trip the vessel sank, without loss of life, on the 7th October, about 170 miles from Boston. Her sister, the "Hibernia," was so badly disabled on the 18th March 1861, in the course of her delivery from Newcastle, that she had to be taken into Liverpool for repairs. The "Columbia" ran her trials on the 28th March, when a speed of 13·9 knots was attained, instead of the stipulated 20 statute miles per hour of the mail contract.[174] She left Galway for her maiden trip on the 9th April, and took 17 days 20 hrs. 45 min. to reach Boston. She returned in May disabled by ice. As the result of many accidents at sea, and the inability of their ships to realise the mail contract speed, the Galway Line was wound up in 1864. The "Anglia" and the "Columbia" were sold to the Turkish Government in 1869, and the "Hibernia" to the Telegraph

Construction and Maintenance Co., in whose service she was wrecked near Aspinwall in 1870.

Principal dimensions of the P.S. "Connaught" were as follows:— Gross register, 2860 tons; net, 1522 tons; displacement, 4400 tons; length over all, 378 ft.; length between perps., 360 ft.; breadth of hull, 40 ft.; breadth over paddle boxes, 71·5 ft.; depth, 29·3 ft.; mean draught, 17·2 ft.

P.S. "SCOTIA" (1861)

The last and finest paddle-driven vessel of the Cunard Steamship Co. Ltd. was the "Scotia," built of iron by Messrs. Robert Napier and Sons, at Glasgow, and launched on the 25th June 1861. She crossed the Atlantic in 1863, from New York to Queenstown, in the record time of 8 days 3 hrs., and held the Blue Riband[175] from 1862 to 1867. She remained on the North Atlantic service for 13 years, the last of the paddle steamers.

The vessel was fitted with six transverse bulkheads, which divided the hull into seven water-tight compartments; she also had four subsidiary or caisson compartments, and was fitted with a double bottom. The hull was bound from stem to stern by five keelsons, all of which were firmly secured at each bulkhead. Her bow framing was arranged diagonally, in order to afford the greatest possible resistance in case of collision.[176] At the time of her launch, the "Scotia" was admitted to be the strongest-built merchant steamer afloat.[177] The weight of iron in her hull alone was 2800 tons. She was rigged as a two-masted brig (see Plate IX); the masts were 30 in. diam. Accommodation for 300 passengers was provided, and 1400 tons of cargo could be carried.

The "Scotia" was propelled by side-lever engines of 975 nominal h.p., constructed by Messrs. Robert Napier and Sons, with two cylinders 100 in. diam. by 12 ft. stroke, which indicated 4570 total h.p. Steam at 25 lb. per sq. in. pressure was supplied by eight tubular boilers, of about 27,600 sq. ft. total heating surface. These contained in all 40 furnaces with a total grate area of about 860 sq. ft. The coal bunkers provided for 1800 tons, while the fuel consumption amounted to about 180 tons per day. The paddle-wheels were 40 ft. diam., and were each fitted with 28 fixed radial floats 11·5 ft. long and 2 ft. wide. On her trials, the "Scotia" is stated to have attained a speed of 16·5 knots; her mean Atlantic speed was 13·5 knots.

Her last trip for the Cunard Steamship Co. Ltd. was made in September 1875. She was afterwards sold to the Telegraph Construction and Maintenance Co., in 1879, and converted into a twin-screw cable ship. For this purpose, she was fitted with inverted two-stage expansion engines of 550 nominal h.p. by Messrs. Laird Bros.; the cylinders were 38 in. and 66 in. diam. by 45 in. stroke. While at sea on this duty in 1896, there was a severe explosion on board, which blew out the bow and destroyed the collision bulkhead. The second bulkhead (44 ft. from the stem) held, however, and saved the vessel from foundering. In 1904 she was wrecked at Guam,[178] in the Ladrone Islands.

Principal dimensions of the P.S. "Scotia" were as follows:— Gross register, 3871 tons; net, 2125 tons; displacement, 6520 tons; length over all, 400 ft.; length between perps., 379 ft.; length of keel, 367 ft.; breadth of hull, 47·8 ft.; breadth over paddle boxes, 76·5 ft.; depth of hold, 30·5 ft.; mean draught, 20 ft.

P.S. "BANSHEE" (1862)

The first steel-built vessel to cross the North Atlantic (and one of the earliest steel ships ever laid down) was the P.S. "Banshee," a blockade-runner used in the American Civil War. She was built for Messrs. John T. Lawrence and Co., at Liverpool in 1862, by Messrs. Jones, Quiggin and Co., who later specialised in the construction of steel blockade-runners; the "Banshee" was the first of a fleet which soon became notorious.

The outbreak of the American Civil War, and the blockade of Confederate ports by the Northerners, resulted in much profitable trade to Liverpool, whose manufactures and munitions were sorely needed by the Southern States in return for the raw cotton required in the Lancashire mills. At first, many of the fastest British coastal, cross-channel and river steamers were put into service; but later, as the blockade became more severe and the number of captures increased, special fast vessels were constructed of steel, which exercised a permanent influence on the subsequent development of steamers in the North Atlantic trade.

The "Banshee" was a schooner, with two pole masts set at a pronounced rake, with small crosstrees for the look-out, but no yards. Her hull was modelled to extremely fine lines, and was built up of steel plates 0·125 in. to 0·188 in. thick on an iron framework.[179] Four water-tight bulkheads were used; one about 30 ft. from bow and stern, and one at either end of the engine-room. The vessel had a turtle-back deck forward, to maintain speed in a seaway, and an elliptical stern. She had two funnels. In the blockade, about 200 tons cargo could be carried in the holds and on deck. The crew numbered 36 men, and four lifeboats were carried.

The machinery of the "Banshee" was of 120 nominal h.p., constructed by Messrs. Laird Bros., of Birkenhead, with two oscillating cylinders 52 in. diam. by 48 in. stroke,[180] which developed about 350 indicated h.p. Steam at 30 lb. per sq. in. pressure was supplied by two steel boilers, one forward and one aft of the engine-room. These boilers were made so low in the vessel, as a protection from shot, that there was insufficient steam space. The coal consumption at full steam is said[181] to have been at the rate of 30 tons per day. The bunkers carried 100 tons. The paddle-wheels were 17·3 ft. diam., each with 14 steel feathering floats 4·3 ft. long and 26 in. wide, and made about 27 revs. per min. at the normal speed of 11 knots. In service, however, the vessel could not be relied upon for more than about 10 knots.

The "Banshee" was completed early in 1863, and left Liverpool on the 2nd March, under the command of Captain J. Steele, and with Mr. Thomas E. Taylor (representative of the owners) on board. Her hull plates became leaky, and she was compelled to put into Cork for repairs. However, she reached Nassau without further mishap, to commence her clandestine vocation. The "Banshee" had many narrow escapes, and was captured on her ninth trip, near Cape Hatteras[182] on the 21st November 1863.

She was acquired by the United States Navy, and put into service on the 12th March 1864 to enforce the blockade which she had earlier defied. She was not, however, very successful in this service; and after the war she was sold for the mercantile marine, renamed the "J. L. Smallwood," and used for cattle transport across the Gulf of Mexico to the island of Cuba. She was later sold for the second time, renamed the P.S. "Irene," and put on service to the Bahama Islands.

Principal dimensions of the P.S. "Banshee" were as follows:— Gross register, 325 tons; net, 217 tons; displacement, about 470 tons; length over all, about 220 ft.; length between perps., 214 ft.; breadth of hull, 20 ft.; breadth over paddle boxes, 33·3 ft.; depth of hold, about 10 ft.; draught, 8 ft.

P.S. "WASHINGTON" (1863)

This was the first of three paddle steamers ordered by the Compagnie Générale Transatlantique, for the French Line mail service between Havre and New York.[183] The vessel was built of iron by Messrs. Scott and Co., at Greenock, and launched on the 17th June 1863. Her two sister-ships, the "Lafayette" and the "Europe," were also launched at Greenock, in 1863 and 1864 respectively. The "Impératrice Eugénie" (1864) and four other similar vessels (most of them built at the Chantiers de Penhoët, at St. Nazaire,[184] with the help of technicians and workmen sent over from Messrs. Scott and Co., Greenock) were also launched for the French Line in 1864-65, and these were the last paddle steamers constructed for the Atlantic service.

The "Washington" was constructed with four keelsons under the engine-room, which was enclosed fore and aft by transverse water-tight bulkheads. The frames were all double, and were spaced 20 in. apart; those under the engine-room were reinforced. The hull plates varied in thickness from 1 in. to 0·63 in., and were double-riveted. The horizontal seams were overlapped in alternate strakes; the vertical seams were flush. The hull plates were also double-riveted to the keel, and to the stem and sternpost.[185]

The vessel had four decks, of which the weather-deck was flush from stem to stern; the depth between decks was 7·25 ft. The deck beams consisted each of a strip with two angle-irons; these were spaced 40 in. apart, bent over at the ends, and riveted to the frames. The supports for the outer bearings of the paddle-wheels were attached to the outer plating of the hull. Accommodation was provided for a total of 330 passengers, and the holds provided, in the first instance, for 1000 tons of cargo. The vessel carried three masts and two funnels.

The machinery was constructed by the Greenock Foundry Co., and consisted of a pair of side-lever engines of 850 nominal h.p.,[186] each mounted on a foundation plate cast in one piece with the condenser, and bolted to the keelsons. The two cylinders were 94·5 in. diam. by 104 in. stroke, and developed a total of 3200 indicated h.p. Double slide valves were used for the steam distribution. The side-levers were of malleable iron, then a novelty; each was 24 ft. long and 7 ft. deep in the centre.[187] The cast-iron entablature was supported by four columns of malleable iron, and braced by two oblique struts.

Steam at a pressure of about 25 lb. per sq. in. was supplied by four return-tube boilers, 22 ft. long, 12 ft. wide and 14 ft. high, two placed forward of the engine-room and two abaft. Each boiler contained 284 brass tubes and six furnaces. The total heating surface was 15,000 sq. ft., and the total grate area 508 sq. ft. The boilers were entirely encased in sheet iron, spaced 2 in. from the boilers and dismountable in sections. The coal consumption was about 125 tons per day; the bunkers carried 1500 tons.[188] The paddle-wheels were 36 ft. diam., each with 28 fixed radial floats 11 ft. long and 2 ft. wide, and rotated at 16·5 revs. per min. for the normal speed of 13 knots.

Before the vessel was delivered from Greenock to her base at St. Nazaire in 1864, she steamed 16 statute miles in 61 min., at a speed of 13·7 knots. For her maiden trip, she left Havre on the 15th June 1864;[189] she met heavy weather on the Atlantic, but reached New York in ten days at a mean speed of 13 knots. In 1867 the vessel was converted to twin-screw propulsion. She was the first Atlantic liner to be fitted with twin screws, which increased her speed to 13·75 knots. Her fuel consumption was reduced; but this was partly due to the installation of new surface condensers. The cargo space was, at the same time, increased to 1350 tons. Later, in 1873, she was refitted with two compound inverted engines of 500 nominal h.p., each with cylinders 47 in. and 84·5 in. diam. by 36 in. common stroke, constructed in France by Messrs. Schneider et Cie., Creusot.

The other French Line paddle steamers were also converted to screw propulsion. The "Europe" was lost at sea in 1874. The "Impératrice Eugénie" was renamed the "Atlantique," and later the "Amérique." This vessel was in 1873 lengthened to 393 ft., and thereby increased to 4584 tons. She ran ashore at New Jersey on the 7th January 1877, and it was not until the 10th April that she was refloated and towed to port. In 1895 she was lost at Cerizoles Point, near Sabanilla. The "Washington" was sold for scrap in 1899 at Marseilles. The "Lafayette" was likewise sold in 1906, and broken up at Brest.

Principal dimensions of the P.S. "Washington" (1863) were as follows:—Gross register, 3408 tons; net, 2091 tons; displacement, 5670 tons; length between perps., 345·7 ft.; breadth of hull, 43·7 ft.; breadth over paddle boxes, about 70 ft.; depth, 30·2 ft.; mean draught, 20 ft.

F

P.S. "COLONEL LAMB" (1864)

The blockade-runner "Banshee" (see p. 68) of the American Civil War, was soon followed by another famous vessel the "Colonel Lamb," built likewise of steel by Messrs. Jones, Quiggin and Co., at Liverpool, to the order of Mr. J. B. Lafitte, of Nassau, and launched in May 1864. She was later owned by Messrs. Fraser, Trenholm and Co., of the Confederacy, and named after the famous commandant of Fort Fisher. She and her sister-ship the "Hope," launched at Liverpool[190] on the 25th November 1863, are stated to have been the fastest and most successful of the blockade-runners built in Great Britain.

The "Colonel Lamb" was a schooner, with two funnels and two pole masts set at a pronounced rake. Her hull was built on a steel framework, and was subdivided by four water-tight transverse bulkheads of steel plate 0·188 in. thick. The decks were of yellow pine. She had the traditional turtle-back deck forward,[191] and an elliptical stern. She carried 2500 bales of cotton, equivalent to about 560 tons, and her crew consisted of 50 officers and men. Two quarter-boats were carried forward of the paddle-wheels, and four lifeboats aft.

The vessel was fitted by Messrs. James Jack and Co., of Liverpool, with fore-and-aft engines of 350 nominal h.p.[192] These comprised two oscillating cylinders about 72 in. diam. by 72 in. stroke, which it is probable would have developed about 1300 indicated h.p., and which were fitted with surface condensers.[193] Steam at a pressure of about 30 lb. per sq. in. was supplied by four steel boilers, two placed forward of the engine-room, and two aft. The coal consumption was about 55 tons per day; some 270 tons were carried in the bunkers. The paddle-wheels were 25·7 ft. diam., each with ten feathering steel floats 7·75 ft. long and 3 ft. wide, and made 30 revs. per min. On her trials in September 1864, the vessel attained a speed of 16·7 knots in heavy seas and head-winds.

The "Colonel Lamb" proved very troublesome to the Northerners. She was described as a "long, low, rakish vessel, at present light lead colour." A report from the U.S. Consulate, Liverpool, dated the 7th September 1864, states: "Enclosed is a description of the new steel steamer 'Colonel Lamb,' just finished at this port. This is one of the largest and best built steamers that has been constructed in this country for running the blockade. . . . I understand this vessel has been built for the Confederacy and now belongs to them. . . . I regard her as a very superior steamer. If armed with one or two guns she would be able to do much mischief as a privateer." Another official report, dated the 27th October 1864, mentions the belief that the "Colonel Lamb" was to be converted into a privateer, so that fear of her seems to have been most pronounced. She was commanded by the well-known Captain Tom Lockwood.

Her sister-ship the P.S. "Hope," which had been commanded by Captain W. J. Gill, was sold at Boston in 1865. At the end of the war, the "Colonel Lamb" arrived back in Liverpool on the 30th May 1865. She was then sold to the Brazilian Government, and chartered to take a cargo of explosives across the Atlantic. Before her departure, however, while riding at anchor in the Mersey, she blew up; and thus ended violently her adventurous career.[194]

Principal dimensions of the P.S. "Colonel Lamb" were as follows:—Gross register, 1132 tons; net, 688 tons; displacement 1790 tons; length over all, 296 ft.; length between perps., 281 ft., breadth of hull, 34·6 ft.; breadth over paddle boxes, 55·3 ft.; depth, 16·7 ft.; draught, 11 ft. She and the "Banshee" are included here as transatlantic pioneers of steel hull construction, a technical development which came too late for the French Line paddle steamers, or the famous Cunard P.S. "Scotia" (see p. 67). These earlier vessels of iron, however, represented the final and finest development in Atlantic paddle steamers, before their clumsy old paddles were superseded by the more efficient screw propeller.

REFERENCES

1. Monleón, Rafael, *Las carabelas de Colón*. Madrid, 1891. *La nao "Santa María."* Madrid, 1892.
2. Clark, Arthur H., *The clipper ship era*. New York, 1911.
3. Spratt, H. Philip, *The birth of the steamboat*. London, 1958.
4. Further technical data on the paddle steamers described in Chapter I will be found in Tables I and II.
5. Mitman, Carl W., *Catalogue of the Watercraft Collection in the United States National Museum*. Washington, 1923, p. 61.
6. New York Custom House Records. *Nautical Gazette*, New York, 14th January 1909, p. 27.
7. Marestier, Jean Baptiste, *Mémoire sur les bateaux à vapeur des États-Unis d'Amérique*. Paris, 1824, p. 71.
8. Partington, Charles Frederick, *An historical and descriptive account of the steam engine*. London, 1822, p. 68. *Journal of Arts and Sciences*, London, Vol. I, 1820, p. 147.
9. *New York Mercantile Advertiser*, New York, 27th March 1819.
10. Bolton, H. C., "The log-book of the 'Savannah.'" *Harper's New Monthly Magazine*, New York, February 1877, p. 342.
11. Watkins, J. Elfreth, "Log of the 'Savannah.'" *Report of the United States National Museum*, Washington, 1890.
12. *Scientific American*, New York, 14th October 1854.
13. Preserved in the United States National Museum at Washington.
14. *The Times*, London, 30th June 1819.
15. *Christiansands Adresse-Contoirs Efterretninger*, Christiansand, 3 November 1819, p. 3.
16. Hunt's *Merchants' Magazine and Commercial Review*, New York, December 1850, p. 693.
17. *Daily National Intelligencer*, Washington, 18th December 1819.
18. Gilfillan, S. C., "The first seagoing auxiliary." *Yachting*, New York, July 1930, p. 54. Tyler, David B., *Steam conquers the Atlantic*. New York, 1939, p. 14.
19. *The Mariners' Museum*, 1930-1950. Publication No. 20, Mariners' Museum, Newport News, Va., 1950, p. 35.
20. Holmes, Sir G. C. V., *Ancient and modern ships*. London, 1906, Part II, p. 14.
21. *Gazeta de Lisboa*, Lisbon, 19 Outubro 1820.
22. *Parliamentary Papers*, London, 1837-38, No. 78, XLV, pp. 30-31.
23. Marestier, Jean Baptiste, *Mémoire sur les bateaux à vapeur des États-Unis d'Amérique*. Paris, 1824, p. 178.
24. Maudslay Society, *Henry Maudslay, 1771-1831; and Maudslay, Sons and Field*. Bedford, 1949, p. 44.
25. *Parliamentary Papers*, London, 1822, No. 417, VI, p. 199.
26. *The Engineer*, London, 24th September 1897, p. 297; and 15th October 1897, p. 368.

27. Graham, Maria, *Journal of a residence in Chile*. London, 1824, p. 173.
28. Dundonald, Tenth Earl of, *Narrative of services in the liberation of Chili, Peru, and Brazil from Spanish and Portuguese domination*. London,' 1859, Vol. I, pp. 204-205.
29. *Histoire de la marine*. Éditée par *Illustration*, Paris, 1934, p. 340.
30. Spratt, H. Philip, "Le premier vapeur transatlantique de la France." *Revue Trimestrielle Canadienne*, Montréal, Hiver 1950-51, p. 410.
31. Bibliothèque Nationale, Paris. Département des Manuscrits, Nouvelles acquisitions, France, No. 9483.
32. Archives Centrales de la Marine, Paris. Service Historique, 7 DD[1], p. 10.
33. Tourasse, M., et Mellet, F. N., *Essai sur les bateaux à vapeur*. Paris, 1828-29, p. 126.
34. *Moniteur Universel*, Paris, 29 Juillet 1824.
35. Tourasse, M., et Mellet, F. N., *op. cit.*, p. 102.
36. Information received from Contre-Amiral M. Adam, C.B.E., from the files of Pierre Le Conte, and from Amiral Pierre Rouyer.
37. Archives Centrales de la Marine, Paris. Service Historique, CC[1]-1074, folio 1996.
38. Tourasse, M., et Mellet, F. N., *op. cit.*, p. 127.
39. Nouhuys, Jan W. van, *De eerste Nederlandsche transatlantische stoomvaart in 1827 van Zr. Ms. stoompakket "Curaçao."* 's-Gravenhage, 1927. See also: "'S Konings stoom packet 'Curaçao.'" *Marineblad*, 's-Gravenhage, Februari 1923.
40. Royal United Service Museum, *Official Catalogue*. London, 1920, p. 278.
41. Clowes, W. Laird, *The Royal Navy*. London, 1903, Vol. VI, p. 271.
42. *Parliamentary Papers*, London, 1849, No. 305, XVII, p. 66.
43. Campbell, Archibald, "The 'Royal William,' the pioneer of ocean steam navigation." *Transactions of the Literary and Historical Society of Quebec*, Quebec, New Series, No. 20, 1891.
44. *Quebec Gazette*, Quebec, 28th April 1831, p. 2.
45. Article on Mr. John Bennet. *Daily Witness*, Montreal, Saturday, 20th March 1897.
46. Letter from Mr. George Black. *Quebec Morning Chronicle*, Quebec, 11th January 1884.
47. Ker, Robert, "The pioneer of Atlantic steamships." *Canadian Magazine*, Toronto, May 1907, p. 13.
48. Wurtële, F. C., "S.S. 'Royal William,' the pioneer of transatlantic steam navigation." Appendix G, *Report of the Secretary of State of Canada for 1894*. Ottawa, 1895, p. 60.
49. Letter from Mr. Alexander Somerville. *Toronto Globe*, Toronto, 15th May 1876. See also: Spratt, H. Philip, "El 'Royal William.'" *Revista General de Marina*, Ministerio de Marina, Madrid, Tomo 134, Abril 1948, p. 537.
50. Folder entitled "The story of the 'Royal William.'" Royal Bank of Canada, Montreal, 1933.
51. Museo Naval, *Catálogo Guía del Museo Naval de Madrid*. Madrid, 1934, p. 166.
52. Wood, William, "The record-making 'Royal William.'" *Canadian Geographical Journal*, Montreal, August 1933, p. 53.
53. This is the official Canadian measurement, based on the over-all breadth of the hull, which was flared out to envelop the paddle-wheels as described. This unusual construction rendered her calculated measurement dis-

F*

proportionate to her burden, as compared with other pioneer Atlantic steamships.

54. *Edinburgh Philosophical Journal*, Edinburgh, January 1820.
55. Hall, Samuel, *Improvements in steam-engines*. Specification No. 6556, Great Seal Patent Office, London, 13th February 1834.
56. Field, Joshua, *Glances at Atlantic steam navigation*, 1838-41. Manuscript in Science Museum Library, London.
57. Barry, William J., "History of the 'Sirius.' " *Journal of the Cork Historical and Archæological Society*, Cork, October-December 1905, p. 159.
58. Further technical data on the paddle steamers described in Chapter II will be found in Tables I and II.
59. *New York Herald*, New York, 24th April 1838.
60. Sheppard, Thomas, "The 'Sirius,' the first steamer to cross the Atlantic." *Mariner's Mirror*, Society for Nautical Research, London, January 1937, p. 90.
61. Field, Joshua, *op. cit.*, p. 6.
62. Port of Bristol Authority, *Short history of the S.S. "Great Western."* Bristol, 1938, p. 21.
63. Farr, Grahame E., "The 'Great Western.' " *Mariner's Mirror*, Society for Nautical Research, London, April 1938, p. 151.
64. Stanton, Samuel W., "The earliest transatlantic steamships." *Engineering Magazine*, New York, September 1895, p. 1051.
65. *Mechanics' Magazine*, London, 6th October 1838, p. 16.
66. Field, Joshua, *op. cit.*, p. 18.
67. *Liverpool Mercury*, Liverpool, 12th October 1838.
68. Field, Joshua, *op. cit.*, p. 24.
69. Field, Joshua, *op. cit.*, p. 30.
70. *New York Herald*, New York, 24th April 1838.
71. Sandham, Henry, "On the history of paddle-wheel steam navigation." *Proceedings*, Institution of Mechanical Engineers, London, March 1885, p. 137.
72. Douglas, James, *The S.S. "Unicorn."* Quebec, 1910.
73. *The Artizan*, London, September 1849, p. 202.
74. Field, Joshua, *op. cit.*, p. 47.
75. Dartnell, Geo. R., *Brief narrative of the shipwreck of the transport "Premier."* London, 1845, pp. 30-31.
76. Heyl, Erik, *Early American steamers*. Buffalo, 1956, Vol. II, p. 259.
77. Field, Joshua, *op. cit.*, p. 43.
78. *The Times*, London, 14th April 1841; and 16th April 1841.
79. *The Novascotian*, Halifax, 12th July 1838.
80. *Parliamentary Papers*, London, 1846, No. 45, pp. 3-5.
81. MacMechan, Archibald, *Samuel Cunard*. Toronto, 1930.
82. Further technical data on the paddle steamers described in Chapter III will be found in Tables III and IV.
83. Cunard Steamship Co. Ltd., *The Cunard Line*. London, 1894, p. 13.
84. Dickens, Charles, *American notes*. Fireside edition, London, 1903, p. 14.
85. Field, Joshua, *op. cit.*, p. 48.
86. *Liverpool Mercury*, Liverpool, 3rd July 1840.
87. *The Artizan*, London, September 1849, p. 204.
88. *The Artizan*, London, December 1849, p. 268.
89. Fincham, John, *History of naval architecture*. London, 1851, p. 321.
90. *The Times*, London, 9th April 1847.

91. *Civil Engineer and Architect's Journal*, London, March 1843, p. 107.
92. *The Albion*, Liverpool, 18th February 1850.
93. *New York Herald*, New York, 31st January 1847.
94. *New York Herald*, New York, 26th May 1847.
95. Austin, J., "Liverpool and the Atlantic ferry." *Proceedings*, Institution of Mechanical Engineers, London, June 1934, p. 93.
96. Tredgold, Thomas, *Steam navigation*. London, 1851, Second Paper, p. 25.
97. *The Artizan*, London, December 1854, p. 281.
98. Kemble, John H., "Hundred years of the Pacific mail." *American Neptune*, Salem, Mass., April 1950, p. 134.
99. Stanton, Samuel W., "The earliest transatlantic steamships." *Engineering Magazine*, New York, September 1895, p. 1057. See also: Spratt, H. Philip, "Le premier transatlantique à vapeur 'United States.' " *Revue Maritime*, Service Historique de la Marine, Paris, Avril 1953, p. 503.
100. *American Neptune*, Peabody Museum, Salem, Mass., October 1944, p. 306.
101. *Illustrated London News*, London, 29th April 1848, p. 281.
102. Goodrich, Caspar F., "America's part in founding the German Navy." *Proceedings*, United States Naval Institute, Annapolis, February 1924, p. 212.
103. *The Artizan*, London, August 1849, p. 174.
104. *The Artizan*, London, July 1858, p. 177.
105. *Illustrated London News*, London, 26th June 1858, p. 642.
106. *The Times*, London, 26th November 1858, p. 5.
107. *New York Herald*, New York, 30th November 1858.
108. *The Times*, London, 30th November 1858, p. 10.
109. *The Times*, London, 25th July 1862, p. 5.
110. New York Custom House Records, New York, No. 156, 7th April 1848.
111. Chambers, William, *Things as they are in America*. London, 1854, pp. 7-11 and 20.
112. Austin, J., "Liverpool and the Atlantic ferry." *Proceedings*, Institution of Mechanical Engineers, London, June 1934, pp. 83-122, Table I.
113. Stanton, Samuel W., "The earliest transatlantic steamships." *Engineering Magazine*, New York, September 1895, p. 1060.
114. Morrison, John H., *History of American steam navigation*. New York, 1903, p. 409.
115. *The Artizan*, London, August 1853, p. 185.
116. *The Artizan*, London, July 1853, p. 155.
117. Tredgold, Thomas, *Steam navigation*. London, 1851, Second Paper. p. 29.
118. *The Engineer*, London, 4th April 1856, p. 181.
119. Heyl, Erik, "Two early American passenger liners." *Marine News*, New York, February 1946, p. 93.
120. Cunard Steamship Co. Ltd., *The Cunard Line*. London, 1894, p. 74.
121. Johnson, William, *Imperial cyclopædia of machinery*. Glasgow, 1852-56, Table appendix.
122. *The Albion*, Liverpool, 2nd February 1852.
123. *The Artizan*, London, February 1856, p. 31.
124. Smith, Arthur D. H., *Commodore Vanderbilt*. New York, 1927.
125. *The Artizan*, London, July 1853, p. 164.
126. Choules, Rev. John Overton, *The cruise of the steam yacht "North Star."* Boston, 1854.

127. *The Artizan*, London, May 1855, p. 108.
128. Metzman, Gustav, *Commodore Vanderbilt* (1794-1877). Newcomen Society, New York, 1946, p. 11.
129. *The Artizan*, London, June 1855, p. 129.
130. Heyl, Erik, "Two early American passenger liners." *Marine News*, New York, February 1946, p. 141.
131. *The Artizan*, London, May 1855, p. 108.
132. *The Artizan*, London, May 1855, p. 119.
133. *The Artizan*, London, September 1856, p. 212.
134. Kemble, John H., "Hundred years of the Pacific mail." *American Neptune*, Salem, Mass., April 1950, p. 134.
135. *The Artizan*, London, July 1855, p. 159.
136. *The Engineer*, London, 7th March 1856, p. 129.
137. *The Artizan*, London, January 1856, p. 13.
138. *The Engineer*, London, 29th March 1861, p. 206.
139. *The Engineer*, London, 15th October 1858, p. 306.
140. *The Artizan*, London, February 1856, p. 35.
141. *The Engineer*, London, 4th January 1856, p. 17.
142. *The Artizan*, London, March 1856, p. 56.
143. *The Artizan*, London, September 1856, p. 212.
144. *The Engineer*, London, 17th June 1859, p. 420.
145. *Mariner's Mirror*, Society for Nautical Research, London, April 1920, p. 125.
146. Lytle, William M., *Merchant steam vessels of the United States*, 1807-1868. Steamship Historical Society of America, Mystic, Conn., 1952, p. 193.
147. *The Engineer*, London, 24th October 1856, p. 574.
148. *The Engineer*, London, 26th December 1856, p. 691.
149. *The Engineer*, London, 27th April 1860, p. 267.
150. *The Artizan*, London, April 1856, p. 85.
151. *The Artizan*, London, September 1856, p. 212.
152. Spratt, H. Philip, et Bigot, Germaine L., "Le premier bateau à vapeur en fer." *Revue Maritime*, Service Historique de la Marine, Paris, Noël 1953, pp. 1549-1552.
153. *The Artizan*, London, March 1858, p. 72; and April 1858, p. 98. *Engineering*, London, 3rd January 1958, p. 17.
154. Spratt, H. Philip, "The first steel-hulled Atlantic steamers." *Nautical Magazine*, Glasgow, October 1953, pp. 213-215.
155. Further technical data on the paddle steamers described in Chapter IV will be found in Tables V and VI.
156. *The Artizan*, London, April 1856, p. 85.
157. *Engineering*, London, 31st March 1893, p. 392.
158. *The Artizan*, London, February 1856, p. 45.
159. *The Artizan*, London, November 1854, p. 261.
160. *The Artizan*, London, November 1858, p. 281.
161. Smith, W. H., and Son, *Pictorial history of the "Great Eastern" steam-ship*. London, 1860, p. 1.
162. Russell, J. Scott, *The "Great Eastern" steam-ship*. London, 1857, p. 7.
163. *The Times*, London, 20th April 1857.
164. Walton, Thomas, *Steel ships: their construction and maintenance*. London, 1904, p. 136.
165. Brunel, Isambard, *The life of Isambard Kingdom Brunel*. London, 1870, p. 341. See also: Dugan, James, *The great iron ship*. London, 1953, p. 26.

166. Grantham, John, *Iron ship-building: with practical illustrations.* London, 1868, p. 158.
167. Spratt, H. P., *Marine engineering.* Science Museum, London, 1953, Part II, p. 27.
168. Russell, J. Scott, *The modern system of naval architecture.* London, 1865, Vol. III, Plate 161, Fig. 5.
169. *The Artizan,* London, February 1863, p. 33.
170. *The Engineer,* London, 30th October 1891, p. 356.
171. *The Engineer,* London, 27th April 1860, p. 270.
172. *The Artizan,* London, May 1863, p. 114.
173. *The Engineer,* London, 15th March 1861, p. 182.
174. *The Engineer,* London, 5th April 1861, p. 220. *The Artizan,* London, April 1863, p. 93.
175. *The Artizan,* London, September 1863, p. 213.
176. *The Engineer,* London, 28th June 1861, p. 389.
177. Willow, John, *The steam fleet of Liverpool.* Liverpool, 1865, p. 17.
178. *Daily Graphic,* London, Tuesday, 15th March 1904.
179. Wardle, Arthur C., "Some blockade-runners of the Civil War." *American Neptune,* Salem, Mass., April 1943, p. 134.
180. Morrison, John H., *Iron and steel hull steam vessels of the United States, 1825-1905.* Steamship Historical Society of America, Salem, Mass., 1945, p. 19.
181. Liverpool Public Museum, *Handbook and Guide to the Shipping Gallery.* Liverpool, 1932, p. 56.
182. Taylor, Thomas E., *Running the blockade.* London, 1912, p. 84.
183. Barbance, Marthe, *Histoire de la Compagnie Générale Transatlantique: un siècle d'exploitation maritime.* Paris, 1955, p. 71. *Revue Maritime,* Service Historique de la Marine, Paris, Septembre 1928, p. 335.
184. Chantier et Ateliers de Saint-Nazaire (Penhoët), *Histoire.* Paris, 1950, p. 4.
185. Compagnie Générale Transatlantique, *Rapport de la Commission chargée d'autoriser la mise en service du paquebot de 850 chevaux le "Washington."* Paris, 11 Juin 1864.
186. *The Artizan,* London, July 1863, p. 165.
187. *Illustrated London News,* London, 14th June 1864, p. 473.
188. *The Artizan,* London, November 1863, p. 260.
189. Compagnie Générale Transatlantique, *Histoire, de la mise en service de "Washington" à celle de "Normandie."* Paris, 1939, p. 3.
190. *The Times,* London, 26th November 1863, p. 9.
191. Wardle, Arthur C., "Mersey-built blockade-runners of the American Civil War." *Mariner's Mirror,* Society for Nautical Research, London, July 1942, p. 184.
192. Liverpool Public Museum, *Handbook and Guide to the Shipping Gallery.* Liverpool, 1932, p. 57.
193. *The Artizan,* London, October 1864, p. 237.
194. Spratt, H. P., *Merchant steamers and motor-ships.* Science Museum, London, 1949, Part II, p. 80.

BIBLIOGRAPHY

Barbance, Marthe, *Histoire de la Compagnie Générale Transatlantique*: *un siècle d'exploitation maritime*. Paris, 1955.

Benstead, C. R., *Atlantic Ferry*. London, 1936.

Bonsor, N. R. P., *North Atlantic seaway*. Prescot, 1955.

Bowen, Frank C., *Century of Atlantic travel*. Boston, 1930.

Bradlee, Francis B. C., *The first steamer to cross the Atlantic*. Salem, Mass., 1925.

Braynard, Frank O., *S.S. "Savannah," the elegant steam ship*. University of Georgia, Athens, 1963.

Breittmayer, Albert, *Débuts des bateaux à vapeur*. Lyon, 1895.

Brunel, Isambard, *The life of Isambard Kingdom Brunel*. London, 1870.

Campaignac, A., *De l'état actuel de la navigation par la vapeur*. Paris, 1842.

Chadwick, F. E., *Ocean steamships*. New York, 1891.

Chambers, William, *Things as they are in America*. London, 1854.

Chantier et Ateliers de Saint-Nazaire (Penhoët), *Histoire*. Paris, 1950.

Chatterton, E. Keble, *Steamships and their story*. London, 1910.

Choules, Rev. John Overton, *The cruise of the steam yacht "North Star."* Boston, 1854.

Clark, Arthur H., *The clipper ship era*. New York, 1911.

Clowes, W. Laird, *The Royal Navy*. London, Vol. VI, 1903.

Compagnie Générale Transatlantique, *Histoire, de la mise en service de "Washington" à celle de "Normandie."* Paris, 1939.

Compagnie Générale Transatlantique, *Rapport de la Commission chargée d'autoriser la mise en service du paquebot de 850 chevaux le "Washington."* Paris, 11 Juin 1864.

Cunard Steamship Co. Ltd., *The Cunard Line*. London, 1894.

Dartnell, Geo. R., *Brief narrative of the shipwreck of the transport "Premier."* London, 1845.

Dickens, Charles, *American notes*. Fireside edition, London, 1903.

Douglas, James, *The S.S. "Unicorn."* Quebec, 1910.

Dow, John G., *The Collins Line* (Manuscript thesis, Columbia University, New York), 1937.

Dugan, James, *The great iron ship*. London, 1953.

Dundonald, Tenth Earl of, *Narrative of services in the liberation of Chili, Peru, and Brazil from Spanish and Portuguese domination*. London, Vol. I, 1859.

Field, Joshua, *Glances at Atlantic steam navigation* (Manuscript in Science Museum Library, London), 1838-41.

Fincham, John, *History of naval architecture*. London, 1851.

Flachat, M. E., *Marine à vapeur commerciale*. Paris, 1869.

Fletcher, R. A., *Steam-ships: the story of their development to the present day*. London, 1910.

Fry, Henry, *The history of North Atlantic steam navigation.* New York, 1896.

Gibbs, C. R. Vernon, *Passenger liners of the western ocean.* London, 1952.
Graham, Maria, *Journal of a residence in Chile.* London, 1824.
Grantham, John, *Iron ship-building: with practical illustrations.* London, 1868.

Haldane, J. W. C., *Steamships and their machinery.* London, 1893.
Henderson, Andrew, *On ocean steamers and clipper ships.* Liverpool, 1854.
Heyl, Erik, *Early American steamers.* Buffalo, 1953–56.
Holmes, Sir G. C. V., *Ancient and modern ships.* London, Part II, 1906.

Illustrations, *Historie de la marine.* Paris, 1934.

Jackson, G. G., *The story of the liner.* London, 1931.
Johnson, William, *Imperial cyclopædia of machinery.* Glasgow, 1852–56.

Kennedy, John, *The history of steam navigation.* Liverpool, 1903.
Kennedy, N. W., *Records of the early British steamships.* Liverpool, 1933.
King, Thomas B., *Report on ocean steamers.* Washington, 1846.

Lee, Charles E., *The Blue Riband: the romance of the Atlantic Ferry.* London, 1930.
Lindsay, W. S., *History of merchant shipping and ancient commerce.* London, Vol. IV, 1876.
Liverpool Public Museum, *Handbook and Guide to the Shipping Gallery.* Liverpool, 1932.
Lytle, William M., *Merchant steam vessels of the United States, 1807–1868.* Mystic, Conn., 1952.

MacMechan, Archibald, *Samuel Cunard.* Toronto, 1930.
Maginnis, Arthur J., *The Atlantic Ferry.* London, 1892.
Marestier, Jean Baptiste, *Mémoire sur les bateaux à vapeur des Etats-Unis d'Amérique.* Paris, 1824.
Maudslay Society, *Henry Maudslay, 1771–1831; and Maudslay, Sons and Field.* Bedford, 1949.
Metzman, Gustav, *Commodore Vanderbilt (1794–1877).* New York, 1946.
Miles, Pliny, *The advantages of ocean steam navigation.* Boston, 1857.
Mitman, Carl W., *Catalogue of the Watercraft Collection in the United States National Museum.* Washington, 1923.
Monleón, Rafael, *Las carabelas de Colón.* Madrid, 1891.
Monleón, Rafael, *La nao "Santa Maria".* Madrid, 1892.
Morrison, John H., *History of American steam navigation.* New York, 1903.
Morrison, John H., *Iron and steel hull steam vessels of the United States, 1825–1905.* Salem, Mass., 1945.
Murray, R., *Rudimentary treatise on marine engines and steam vessels.* London, 1868.
Museo Naval, *Catálogo Guia del Museo Naval de Madrid.* Madrid, 1934.

Napier, James, *Life of Robert Napier.* London, 1904.
Nouhuys, Jan W. van, *De eerste Nederlandsche transatlantische stoomvaart in 1827 van wr. Ms. stoompakket "Curacao".* 's-Gravenhage, 1927.

Otway, Robert, *Elementary treatise on steam navigation.* Plymouth, 1837.

Parker, H., and Bowen, F. C., *Mail and passenger steamships of the nineteenth century.* London, 1928.
Partington, Charles Frederick, *An historical and descriptive account of the steam engine.* London, 1822.
Port of Bristol Authority, *Short history of the S.S. "Great Western".* Bristol, 1938.
Preble, Geo. H., *Chronological history of the origin and development of steam navigation.* Philadelphia, 1883.

Rainey, Thomas, *Ocean steam navigation and the ocean post.* New York, 1858.
Ross, Sir John, *Treatise on navigation by steam.* London, 1837.
Royal Bank of Canada, *The story of the "Royal William".* Montreal, 1933.
Royal United Service Museum, *Official Catalogue.* London, 1920.
Russell, J. Scott, *The "Great Eastern" steam-ship.* London, 1857.
Russell, J. Scott, *The modern system of naval architecture.* London, Vol. III, 1865.

Séguin, Marc, *Mémoire sur la navigation à vapeur.* Paris, 1828.
Smith, Arthur D. H., *Commodore Vanderbilt.* New York, 1927.
Smith, E. C., *Short history of naval and marine engineering.* Cambridge, 1938.
Smith, E. W., *Trans-Atlantic passenger ships, past and present.* Boston, Mass., 1947.
Smith, Junius, *Letters upon Atlantic steam navigation.* London, 1841.
Smith, W. H., and Son, *Pictorial history of the "Great Eastern" steam-ship.* London, 1860.
Spears, John R., *The story of the American merchant marine.* New York, 1910.
Spratt, H. Philip, *The birth of the steamboat.* London, 1958.
Spratt, H. P., *Marine Engineering.* Science Museum, London, Part II, 1953.
Spratt, H. P., *Merchant steamers and motor-ships.* Science Museum, London, Part II, 1949.
Stuart, Charles B., *The naval and mail steamers of the United States.* New York, 1853.

Taylor, Thomas E., *Running the blockade.* London, 1912.
Tourasse, M., et Mellet, F. N., *Essai sur les bateaux à vapeur.* Paris, 1828–29.
Town, Ithiel, *Atlantic steamships.* New York, 1838.
Tredgold, Thomas, *Steam navigation.* London, Second Paper, 1851.
Tyler, David B., *Steam conquers the Atlantic.* New York, 1939.

United States National Museum, *Catalogue of the Watercraft Collection.* Washington, 1923.

Verne, Jules, *Une ville flottante.* Paris, 1873.

Walker, James, *The first transatlantic steamer.* London, 1898.
Walton, Thomas, *Steel ships: their construction and maintenance.* London, 1904.
Willow, John, *The steam fleet of Liverpool.* Liverpool, 1865.
Woodcroft, Bennet, *Sketch of the origin and progress of steam navigation.* London, 1848.

INDEX